Holistic Therapy

Holistic Therapy

Overcoming Depression and Anxiety Naturally

First Edition

Emma Mary Gathergood

Holistic Therapy
Emma Mary Gathergood

Published by Aspect Design 2010
Malvern, Worcestershire, United Kingdom.

Designed and Printed by Aspect Design
89 Newtown Road, Malvern, Worcs. WR14 1PD
United Kingdom
Tel: 01684 561567
E-mail: books@aspect-design.net
Website: www.aspect-design.net

Editing and initial design by Shabra Dowson
shabra23@yahoo.co.uk

ISBN 978-1-905795-64-2

This book is dedicated to my wonderful family, including my two sons Alex, Dan, their wives, my daughter Lucy, my six grandchildren Jordan, Phoenix, Leah, Storm, Levi and Raphael and their grandfather, Richard.

Contents

Acknowledgments

I would like to thank firstly my family, all named in the dedication, without whom I would never have experienced all the highs and lows that have contributed to me becoming who I am now. It was these experiences that prompted me to do all the trainings and studies that I am now able to write about with such understanding, having used them all at one time or another to help myself!

Secondly I would like to thank all my dear friends, who have helped me so much on my path. These include Kim, Ann, Alison and Jacquie from Lyme Bay; Cathy and Patrick Whitefield, also John Clements and Palden Jenkins from Glastonbury; plus Carol, Shabra, Numa, Bee and Fran from Malvern. Also, I send thanks to my lovely work mates from Bridport, especially Julie, Wendy and Lou, who made my demanding job in the NHS much more fun.

Thirdly I would like to recognise the tireless help that both Ann Evans and Shabra Dowson have put into the different stages of proof reading, editing, and formatting this book, keeping me going with helpful comments and love in equal measures!

I would also like to thank all the writers, therapists, philosophers and dreamers who have written all the wonderfully informative and uplifting books that cram my bookshelves to bursting point! I never cease to be amazed at how fortunate we are to live at a time when all this wisdom is open and available to us for the price of a book or magazine.

And finally I would like to thank all the clients with whom I have worked over the years, for teaching me that we really can turn stumbling blocks into stepping stones, thus moving beyond our limitations.

Introduction

So what is Holistic Therapy?

Holistic Therapy works to integrate and restore balance to mind, body, spirit and emotions. It accepts the latest research indicating the close relationship with all four parts, and how problems in one area are linked to less obvious issues in all other areas. It includes techniques from a wide range of disciplines including Life Coaching, Gestalt Therapy, Body-Mind Awareness, Mindfulness, Psychosynthesis, Cognitive Behavioural Therapy (CBT), Neuro Linguistic Programming (NLP) and Solution Focused Therapy.

If we are feeling down, we often identify with the unhealthy part of ourselves, mistakenly thinking that is who we are. Holistic Therapy can help to access the strong and healthy parts of ourselves. It then teaches new coping strategies, thinking habits, ideas and most importantly a new awareness of who we REALLY are.

This book is designed as a self-help tool for those suffering from depression or anxiety. It can be used in several different ways, depending on the need:-

- Although the book is written as a whole, each chapter can stand alone, thus enabling anyone to immediately turn to a chapter about a specific problem, be it dealing with

anger, learning to be more assertive, understanding
forgiveness or the specific chapters on either anxiety or
depression.

- At the end of each of the chapters is an exercise. It is
  helpful to take time out from reading to actually do the
  exercise. When we read we learn with our minds.
  However, when we do an exercise we are participating
  experientially, thus using our whole self. This learning is
  deeper and more complete than any learning we do with
  our mind alone, and will be retained by us. We are
  fundamentally holistic beings, so when we experience
  something in a holistic way it becomes integrated into our
  whole being, thus becoming a part of us.

- The various therapies discussed in Part One, can be used
  independently of each other, and have been written as an
  educational resource. They show just some of the many
  possible new and exciting ways of working with
  debilitating symptoms in an easy to read and readily
  understandable way. I hope that you may want to follow
  up the references and investigate ideas that appeal to you
  such as changing negative beliefs, finding inner
  awareness, being more positive or sensing the wisdom
  held in our bodies. Each chapter has a reference to a
  relevant web site for further information.

- Taken as a whole the book is a journey into wholeness
  and healing. It is written from a holistic standpoint. This

includes physical, emotional, mental and spiritual concepts, in keeping with the view of transpersonal psychology, the most modern and comprehensive theory on mental health available to date, and increasingly accepted by mainstream psychiatry.

Having worked as an occupational therapist within the mental health field for forty years, both in the NHS and private sector, I have both trained in and studied a wide variety of therapeutic interventions. Over the last few years I have had the wonderful opportunity of introducing the majority of these techniques to my clients, who were suffering from depression and anxiety, and have been extremely impressed by the results. I have seen the vast majority of my clients improve, some becoming totally well after feeling unable to cope with life for several years. While others who were feeling overwhelmed by a current life crisis, have come through it older and wiser but also more calm and capable than they were before the crisis.

Nearing the age when I would have to retire from the NHS, I decided to put some of these therapeutic ideas together in a book that hopefully will inspire not only those suffering from stress, anxiety and depression, but also those around them whose task it is to assist them back to optimal health.

It has been written largely using the words "us" and "we" rather than "you" in a deliberate attempt to bridge the gap between therapist and client. We are all human first and foremost, and I believe we are on this planet to help each other. Whilst working in London in the sixties I had the privilege of meeting Dr. Ronnie Lang, the eminent psychiatrist and author. The one thought I took on board from him and have used throughout my career is his comment to himself when talking to a client with any mental health problem, "There, but for the grace of God, go I". This deep recognition of our own shared humanity has to be the basis of any therapeutic intervention, if it is to be beneficial.

When first noticing we are depressed or anxious it is important to realise that we are not alone with our problem. Possibly as many as one in four people will experience depression or anxiety at some time in their life. And the good news is there is something that we can do about it.

This book has been written to offer some tools for learning a new skill. And that is the understanding that we are more powerful than we think. We can learn through these chapters to let go of some of the false self-identities, false self-beliefs, and faulty thinking that society, our background, schooling, family and life itself has taught us. We can begin to learn new coping strategies, thinking habits, ideas and most importantly a new awareness of WHO WE REALLY ARE.

We may be amazed to discover that many of the labels we have lived under for years can begin to be replaced with a more positive, upbeat and helpful self-identity.

The worst symptoms of anxiety and depression come from a dissociation from our own centre, and an over identification with our symptoms. Starting from chapter one and continuing throughout the book we are shown how to systematically reverse this trend, and reconnect with our own True Inner Self that has its own innate wisdom.

There are 4 parts to the book:

Part One introduces eight different therapies, with web site references for each.

Part Two looks at using assertiveness and anger management therapeutically.

Part Three has a specific chapter on depression and one on anxiety.

Part Four has a chapter on the role of forgiveness, plus the conclusion, which returns to the theme of chapter one, who we really are.

Part One

Chapter one starts by asking **Who do we think we are?** It discusses the various self-definitions that society has given us, then asks us to look deeper in to the fact we may be more than we think we are. The reader is introduced to the Aware Observer Self through an exercise, with references to Psychosynthesis, a humanistic psychotherapy started by Assaglioli in Italy and brought to England by Diana Bicketti in the 1960s.

We then look at **Awareness of the Three Faces of Self.** This chapter starts by looking at our Mask Self or the face we show to the world. It goes on to discover our Shadow Self or the face we hide from the world. It ends with starting to understand that neither of these are our true identity, and so moving into discovering the face of who we truly are, with an exercise to discover our three faces. This particular model takes the search into who we are a stage deeper.

In studying **Awareness of Limiting Beliefs** we consider the NLP (Neuro Linguistic Programming) approach to how our beliefs influence our behaviour and therefore our experience, and how we can start to change these limiting beliefs. There is an exercise to learn how to do this.

Next we discover **Body Mind Awareness** which looks at the latest scientific discoveries that point to the connection between our body and mind. It explores Reverse Therapy, and how it works by introducing us to the concept of our body's own awareness, helping to overcome chronic fatigue and anxiety.

The next chapter on **Awareness of Solution Focused Therapy and Positive Psychology** explores how these new therapies agree with ancient wisdom about the holistic nature of human beings and the subsequent need for a holistic therapeutic approach. It looks at the most recent research pointing to the importance of using a positive rather than an analytical approach when working with depression.

The next therapy is **CBT and Coping Strategies Awareness** which discusses Cognitive Behavioural Therapy, the therapy recommended by the NICE (National Institute of Health and Clinical Excellence) and available on the NHS, and a simple description of how it works. Also the importance of how to build coping strategies is emphasised.

Then we look at **Mindfulness Awareness** and how this ancient Buddhist practise is now taken up by psychotherapists and used by the NHS to run 8 week courses for people suffering severe stress due to physical or mental illness.

Part Two

In the chapter on **Understanding Assertiveness** we consider how basic assertiveness principles can give everyone more life skills with which to combat depression and stress.

This theme is continued with **Understanding Anger** which looks at how depression and anxiety can be made

worse by suppressing our anger. The chapter also examines
the therapeutic nature of anger when used appropriately. It
considers how we actually experience our own anger and
how we can learn to de-escalate our anger by managing it
successfully.

Part Three

In **Understanding Depression** we look at the nature of
depression, how our thoughts perpetuate it, and how to
change our biochemistry, not just with anti-depressant
medication but also by changing the way we look at life in
general through learning new ways of using our mind.

Then in **Understanding Anxiety** we look at the physical
symptoms associated with anxiety, why they arise, and how
to work with them. Also looking at the Fight/Flight
Response, and the use of CBT, Reverse Therapy or EMDR to
change how we cope with anxiety.

Part Four

Finally we study the **Awareness of the Role of
Forgiveness.** This chapter looks at how a lack of forgiveness
only damages ourselves, so we are injured twice, first by the
aggressor and secondly by ourselves. We consider how we
can choose to forgive as an act of self-love and self-healing.

In the **Conclusion - Ending the case of Mistaken
Identity** the book ends with looking at how our previous
self-identity has contributed to our current depression and

anxiety. By using the new techniques learnt in this book, we can change this false identity for ever. As we have studied each of the previous topics it has led us to an increased awareness of our true nature which no longer needs to identify with our depressed or anxious feelings. We realise they belong to the past, and we can now let them go, learning to live in and identity with our True Self.

I hope you will enjoy reading and working with this book, as much as I have enjoyed researching, developing and writing it.

Emma Mary Gathergood

The Malvern Hills   May 2010

References

1.   **The Psychosynthesis and Educational Trust**
     92 - 94 Tooley Street, London Bridge, SE1 2TH
     www.psychosynthesis.edu
2.   **The Three Faces of Self**
     Emma Gathergood
     emmamarygathergood@ymail.com
3.   **Neuro Linguistic Programming**
     en.wikipedia.org/wiki/Neuro-linguistic_programming
     or contact Emma Mary Gathergood NLP Practitioner
     emmamarygathergood@ymail.com
4.   **Dr. Eaton**
     The Wholistic Medical Centre
     57 Harley Street, London W1G 8QS
     www.reverse-therapy.com
5.   **Positive Psychology**
     www.positivepsychology.org.uk
6.   **Cognitive Behavioural Therapy**
     www.nhs.uk and search for CBT
7.   **Mindfulness Based Cognitive Therapy**
     www.mbct.co.uk
     The Centre for Mindfulness Research and Practice,
     School of Psychology
     Bangor University, LL57 1UT
8.   **EMDR**
     Eye Movement Desensitisation and Reprocessing
     www.emdr-therapy.org

Part One
Introducing Holistic
Therapies

Chapter One

Who do you think you are?

So, who do YOU think you are? You are aware of who your friends and family think you are, but is this a totally complete description? They would probably describe you in terms of age, gender, ethnicity, height, and other such words which would adequately describe your BODY. Then they may speak of your role in the family, your occupation, ways you spend your time, and other such words describing your behaviour and what your BODY does.

In a deeper description they may speak of your attitude to life, how you see things, what sort of things interest you, your views or other descriptions of how your MIND works. Then finally they may speak of your FEELINGS in terms of your predominant moods, sensitivities, preferences. And yet does describing your BODY, MIND and FEELINGS totally describe YOU? Is there more to you than this, an ESSENCE or something intangible that makes you feel you are actually all the above plus something else?

We can spend years being totally absorbed in hectic lives that leave us little time for contemplating "life, the universe and everything!" Then something may cause a trauma in terms of the loss of someone or something close to us that leaves us feeling the carpet has been pulled from under our feet. Suddenly those self-descriptions that previously seemed perfectly adequate no longer suffice. We become depressed and anxious, feeling we have lost our way, no longer so sure of where we are going or, indeed, who we are any more.

It is at times like these that we begin to ask the big questions.... Who am I, and what am I doing with my life? The interesting thing is that as soon as we start to ask these questions we find unusual co-incidences start to happen. "By chance" we are flipping channels on the TV and find a programme where people are discussing the very concept we were thinking about. We are in the library and a book seems to catch our eye that has some answers for us. Or a friend starts to tell us about something they have just heard, little realising we are really interested to hear this information because we have been thinking about this same subject.

Carl Jung, the godfather of transpersonal psychology and a contemporary of Sigmund Freud, calls these co-incidences "synchronicities". They seem to happen out of the blue, but actually are an indication that we are going in the right direction, where we will find the answers to some of our most pressing questions. However what I find the most surprising thing is that these synchronicities only begin to happen when we start to question the status quo, start to inquire in our minds so WHO am I, and what IS the purpose of my life. When we start to ask these kinds of questions, it is

as if we suddenly discover a more aware part of ourselves
that does seem to hold a sort of wisdom of which we were
previously unaware. This aware self never intrudes into our
private space, or tells us answers to questions we have not
asked. It totally respects our free will and our right to choose
our own beliefs and experiences. If we are content to live our
life without questioning anything, happy to live with only
the awareness of body, mind and feelings, then our wise,
aware self will not intrude into our thinking or experience.

BUT, when apparent disaster strikes, this is the time
that all sorts of doors start opening to us, doors that we
always thought were brick walls. Richard Bach in his book
"Illusions" said "What the caterpillar calls the end of the
world, the master calls a butterfly!" If we stop to think about
this for a moment it is clear that from the limited perception
of the caterpillar, when he finds himself squashed up in his
pupa, unable to crawl around, losing the power of his sticky
little legs, this really is disaster!

And it does seem that we go through a similar stage at
the beginning of a period of personal growth. We appear to
be restricted, stuck, unable to move forward in the way we
always have. Nothing is working any more, and we start to
feel lost and frightened. This is only natural, when we realise
nothing will ever be the same again, but instead of that being
the end of the world it is in fact the beginning of a whole
new life, much more beautiful, free, exiting and wonderful.

We truly are about to emerge, after a period of restricted activity, into the amazing world of the butterfly.

This is why I am able to say with total confidence that problems or illness of all kinds, mental or physical is often a wakeup call, but not a disaster. It is possible to turn the stumbling block of ill health into the stepping stone of transformation and healing. Our caterpillar self has become stuck, and whether we realise it or not has orchestrated this life changing challenge that has come our way.

The wonderful thing about looking at life this way is that we can begin to look at our problems or illness in a different way. Dr. Wayne W. Dyer says in "Stop the Excuses!" the encouraging words "When you change the way you look at things, the things you look at change". Let's think about that for a moment. Could it be that if you stop looking at your situation with fear, dread and hostility, but instead, try to make friends with it, it is highly likely that it will change? So you will indeed end up looking at something different as Dr. Dyer says. You will hopefully be looking at and experiencing better mental and physical health and vitality than you ever had before.

After 40 years of research into problem solving and mental health I am absolutely certain this is true, and this is what I aim to prove throughout this book. I plan to provide you with a road map which will enable you to travel to meet your problem, to spend time with it, get to know it, make friends with it, and eventually transform it with love into a whole new you. And as you near the end of this journey you will have a far more definitive and meaningful answer to your question "Who am I?" than you have now.

The following exercise has been adapted from a meditation technique I first learnt when I studied Psychosynthesis Transpersonal Psychology about 30 years ago.

Exercise One

Discovering "Who am I?"

Start by finding a comfortable, quiet space where you will not be disturbed for 20 minutes. Take a few deep breaths, and begin to relax your BODY. Starting with your toes, begin to concentrate on each part of your body in turn. Firstly as you breathe in becoming aware of that part of the body, then as you breathe out letting go of tension there, and allowing that part of the body to relax. Working up through your feet, ankles, calves, knees, thighs, buttocks, back, lower body, stomach area, chest , hands, arms, shoulders, neck, head and scalp, taking up to 10 minutes to totally relax your entire body. Then say to yourself "My body is PART of me but I, MYSELF am MORE than my body".

Then think about your thoughts and your MIND. Start to become aware of your thoughts, watch them come into your field of awareness then watch them leave. Attempt to become an objective observer of your thoughts, just for a few minutes. So instead of actually getting caught up in your thoughts and running with them, for a while watch your thoughts come and go, just as if they were objects arising on a video screen. Watch them come and go with a detached awareness, totally without judgement or preference. Then say to yourself, "My mind is part of me but I, MYSELF am MORE than my mind".

Then think about your FEELINGS. Become aware of any emotion you are experiencing, and just like in the earlier part of the exercise, attempt to become an impartial observer of your feelings. Don't get caught up in the highs or lows of your emotions, just try to watch them as if they were objects coming and going on a video screen. Then say to yourself, "My feelings are part of me but I, MYSELF am MORE than my feelings".

Then finally allow yourself to sink down inside yourself, with a deep sense of peace and relaxation. It has become apparent to you throughout this exercise that there is obviously a "Detached Observer Self" that has been doing the watching and making the statements about being more than your body, mind or feelings. This self is totally impartial, but is also kind, loving, warm, compassionate and caring. It definitely has your best interests at heart, and as you concentrate on its qualities, it does seem to be somehow bigger, more aware, more steady than any part of yourself you have met before. You can if you prefer, not attempt to name this part of you. But, if it feels good you can say, "Yes, I am MORE than my body, mind and feelings. I am also an AWARE OBSERVER SELF, a wise self which is a part of and connected to the Whole".

And before returning from your meditation, ask this Aware Self to show you a symbol, either a flower, plant, rock or something that is meaningful to you, to help you to remember this lovely relaxed comfortable feeling and to

20   Introducing Holistic Therapies

symbolise this essence of who you are. Then slowly stretch, open your eyes and return to your everyday world. You will find if you try to make time every day to do this exercise, within a short time you will begin to feel a sense of being connected to your Core, to a strong inner sense of Awareness, which will be invaluable in your journey into health and well-being.

See Reference No.1

The Psychosynthesis and Educational Trust
92 - 94 Tooley Street, London Bridge, SE1 2TH
www.psychosynthesis.edu

Chapter Two

The Three Faces of Self

There are many different methods of connecting to your Aware Self, and this one I developed many years ago, calling the outer layer the Mask, the middle layer the Shadow, and the inner layer the True Self.

In order to discover more about the TRUE you that lives inside you, beneath both the "Mask Self" you show to the world and the "Shadow Self" you hide from the world, it is essential to be totally honest with yourself about your thoughts and behaviour. In time, as you develop a deeper awareness of these three faces of yourself you will be more able to express WHO YOU TRULY ARE in the world.

The Mask Self

The Mask Self is the face we show to the world. It has been formed throughout our childhood, adolescence and adulthood as a way of trying to express our True Self in the world, but also as a defence against the part of ourselves we don't like and don't want to acknowledge. It is the self that is nice and kind, good at its job, pleasant to our family and who we generally like to think we are. It is the self that we show to our friends, but especially we show it to the people who we want to like us, like a new acquaintance, a new lover or our boss.

It is not unhealthy to have a strong mask self, just as long as we know that is what it is. In fact we sometimes need this self, if we want to project a certain image in order to achieve a specific goal. For example when on an interview for a job, we will want to portray ourselves as confident and knowing what we are talking about, or we know someone else will get the job! Or as a teacher in front of an unruly classroom, we will want to portray ourselves as strict and not to be messed with!

But our Mask Self neither embraces our personal weaknesses, nor yet the inner truth about us. It is important to always remember it is a set of behaviours and a persona we have chosen over the years to use to portray ourselves. So it can become something of a problem to us when we begin to think it is WHO we are. In other words we have fooled ourselves, and that is always a dangerous position to be in. In order to become self-aware we must look beneath the Mask.

The Shadow Self

The Shadow Self is made up of all those parts of ourselves that we prefer to ignore. It includes both our known negative traits, for example a bad temper, being hyper-critical, self-opinionated, self-righteous, self-pitying but also our unknown negative traits, for example coming from a place of guilt, shame, need to control, cruelty, revenge. Most of us are aware of our more obvious flaws, and genuinely work hard to change them.

Apart from these known traits, in childhood our unconscious Shadow Self also developed some rather destructive hidden traits. The unconscious side of our Shadow Self carries even more weight, and influences us far more than our conscious shadow. Invariably it was our only defence against a bewildering and unknown world, where often the very adults we depended upon for our survival, were frightening us with their incomprehensible behaviour. In order to try to make sense of things, our rather limited childhood awareness ends up coming to some rather disastrous false conclusions, which unless we question and reverse in adulthood can continue to dominate our thinking and consequently our experience throughout our lives.

Our True Self

Our True Self, as the name implies, is all that is true about us.

It is WHO WE WOULD HAVE BEEN, if we had been brought up perfectly.

It is WHO WE CAN BE, if we are able to let go of our false beliefs.

It is WHO WE WERE BORN TO BE, if we are willing to seek and find it.

It is WHO WE TRULY ARE, when we are really being ourselves.

This TRUE SELF lies hidden inside us, undaunted and undamaged by the knocks and hardships that life throws at us. The more we are able to look with sincerity and truth at "The Face We Hide from the World", the closer we get to this True Self. Only as we begin to let go of some of the false beliefs we have about ourselves, and also let go of some of the false conclusions we have drawn, are we able to start to act more authentically. As our actions change, and our expectations and beliefs about what we deserve change, only then are we able to start to manifest what we truly want in this world.

Integrating the Three Faces of Self

To give an example, it may be in childhood we were challenged in a certain area of development. For example, we may not have been very academic, but growing up in a clever family we were left feeling inferior. We may have been plain looking but surrounded by beauties. Maybe we were just not sporty or co-ordinated, leaving us feeling awkward and not able to compete with our peers. Maybe our parent's poverty or the area we grew up in put us at a social disadvantage. All of these experiences made us feel uncomfortable, so to compensate and make us feel better, we looked for ways to raise our self-esteem.

We found areas we could excel in. We all have things we are good at, from artistic talents to developing a helpful attitude, from fitness training to becoming a people person, from learning how to make lots of money to making people laugh, and many more. So as we grew up we developed the skills in our chosen area and started to feel better about ourselves. This is how we developed our Mask Self, or the "Face we Show to the World". It was essential we developed along these lines, and we couldn't have made it in the adult world without this successful mask.

However, if we totally block out those early memories, and believe the Mask Self is all we are, we will be forever running from those hidden feelings of insecurity. They will re-emerge at the most inopportune moments, when we are trying hardest to impress and when it is of most importance we come over as successful and confident. These hidden feelings from childhood often haunt us, manifesting as depression or panic attacks.

So the most effective way to understand and heal these difficult memories is to embrace them. When we are willing to commence on a journey of self-mastery and healing, we temporarily turn our back on the face we have always shown, that of our Mask Self, and start on a journey inwards. At first we obviously encounter "The Face we Hide from the

World" or our Shadow Self. Now many people are unnecessarily scared of this process because they believe they only have these two layers, the comfortable and the uncomfortable one! So before we start on an investigation in to what lies inside our Shadow Self, it is important to spend time in our True Self.

As we get to know our True Self, and see that deep down we really are a good, kind, honest person that gives us the confidence to investigate the contents of the Shadow Self. With our new found awareness of who we REALLY are we can begin to challenge some of the things we were told as children.

Are we really no good simply because we are not academically brilliant, beautiful, sporty or wealthy? With the hindsight of maturity we can begin to question whether we ever were actually inferior, or just made to feel that way by some very unkind, narrow minded or equally insecure people simply covering up their insecurities by making us feel small? Armed with this new awareness it is far less frightening to start to look at those feelings we not only hide from the world, but we also hide from ourselves.

We can begin to see the truth of these painful memories and once and for all challenge whether we ever were as inferior as we were led to believe. Does money, looks, physical strength or cleverness actually make us a superior being? Of course not! As adults we know this to be a fact, but unfortunately as children it was not self-evident. We actually believed our accusers, thinking they knew more than we did. But how wrong could we be! We can now refute these old damaging beliefs, clearing out and freeing up the "Face We Hide from the World."

Then having released some of those old negative beliefs about ourselves, we can return to the Mask Self and start to question whether the face we show to the world is actually an accurate portrayal of who we really are. For example, in order to cover up the insecurities we were feeling as young adults, we may have developed some less than optimum ways of facing the world. We may have developed an aloof persona, or an overly thick skin, or an obsession with always having to look our best.

Or we may have become a workaholic, or overly house proud, or a yes person, at everyone else's beck and call, or any number of other less than desirable traits. Once we can see that these traits were developed to protect ourselves from the debilitating false beliefs we were trying so desperately to overcome, we can realise that it may be time to let go of these traits too. Thus the "Face we Show to the World" can become a more authentic representation of our best qualities, not just a front we use to cover up what we are feeling inside.

I believe that in our heart of hearts we know the truth anyway, because our True Self has always been there. However, sometimes that "still, small voice" can be drowned out by the noise of those around us. But now as adults we can wipe the slate clean, replacing the lies of others with the Truth of our own knowing, becoming the loving, beautiful person we were always meant to be.

Exercise Two

Discovering your True Self

Allow yourself about 20 minutes when you won't be disturbed to sit down quietly with pen and paper and write down some answers to the following questions. It is very helpful to buy yourself a small exercise book which can become your Journal. Everyday start to write down helpful thoughts, ideas, quotations or exercises that will, over the next few months help you to grow and change. Your Journal will be a wonderful way of helping you to see just how far you have come since you started your Healing Journey!

What qualities do you portray in your Mask Self? For example you may be efficient, organised and reliable, but you may be seen as bossy and judgemental. Or you may be kind, caring and helpful, but seen as a pushover or a yes person. You may be thoughtful and quiet, but seen as boring or aloof.

What are your most negative known traits in your Shadow Self? These may include a bad temper, being hyper-critical, self-opinionated, self-righteous, self-pitying, angry, nervous, shy, snobbish, condescending, cocky, arrogant, etc.

What could be your unknown negative traits, for example coming from a place of guilt, shame, need to control, cruelty, revenge, inferiority, fear, superiority, etc.

What false conclusions could you have drawn in your childhood that are still influencing you? For example, that because you are so insecure you must cover this up at all costs, and act overly confident, always look immaculate, work harder than anyone else, earn more money, excel at everything you do etc.

What True Self qualities do you possess? For example, deep down are you loving, kind and caring? Are you dependable, conscientious and reliable? Are you honest, sincere, wise, perceptive and fair? Are you courageous, loyal or strong?

What activities are you participating in when you really feel like you?

Are you alone, or who is with you?

What does it feel like to be that you? Describe the sensations, feelings, thoughts. Would you say words like love, peace, unity and joy are part of this experience?

Can you accept that when you are really being your True Self you are actually a very nice person indeed?

Can you also accept that others too must be "very nice people" if they were able to come from their True Self?

Are you able to accept that your True Self is your GOOD self, and therefore most likely the nearest you can get to what some may call your GOD SELF?

Now you know WHO your True Self is, what can your True Self say to your Shadow Self in order to throw some light on its false conclusions, and help it to release them, moving into a more creative and realistic space?

Also what authentic qualities can your True Self begin to allow your Mask Self to show to the world? How can you express your True Self more in the world?

For more information see Reference 2

The Three Faces of Self
Emma Gathergood
emmamarygathergood@ymail.com

Chapter Three

Changing Limiting Beliefs

Have you ever thought what a definitive influence our beliefs have over our lives? I am not talking here about our obviously influential beliefs such as religion and politics. No, I'm talking about those apparently innocuous little beliefs, such as:-

My ex was a really nasty person...

I never stood a chance what with my background...

My sister is the clever (pretty) one in our family...

I will never get over that traumatic incident...

At some stressful and formative moment in our history we made a decision about something and invariably have never reviewed that decision from that day to this. It becomes carved in stone, turning from a decision to a belief, and from there starts to define who we are, what our *take* on life is. Now it may have been absolutely true when we first said it to ourselves, but everything changes over time.

All things are relative, and what appears true from one angle, as we move, grow and change usually can be seen from other points of view as time passes. But unless we give ourselves time and space to periodically review and up-date our beliefs, we may become stuck in an out-dated version of ourselves. It is always much easier to see these unhelpful beliefs in some-one other than ourselves. For a moment, stop and think of a friend or relative who seems to be stuck in either blame, victimhood, low self-esteem, or trauma. What is the statement they repeatedly make about themselves or their life? Maybe you know enough about them and their history to know that statement is not completely factually true.

Let's look back to our four examples. In the first, the person has a poor opinion of their ex-partner. Perhaps you remember their ex, and know he does have one or two redeeming features! In the next example, where the person blames their background, you may know another person with a similar background to your friend who has done very well for themselves. The third one is about the person who is not as clever (or pretty) as her sister. It could be your friend is actually quite bright (or pretty) but because her sister is more so, she has totally minimized her own achievements (or looks). Or, in our last example, where a previous trauma still seems to impact on the person's life. Maybe you can see how well your friend has got her life back together following her loss or trauma but, because she has not reviewed her previous belief, she still *feels* herself to be traumatized.

As humans we are incredibly good at only seeing what we want to see and blocking out from our awareness those situations that make us feel uncomfortable. And what is more uncomfortable than seeing or hearing something we really don't agree with? In general we hate having our beliefs threatened.

Nowhere is this more apparent than when we see people interviewed on the nightly T.V. news, showing shock, horror and disbelief when something horrible has just happened in their area. They don't want to contemplate that the nice quiet area they have chosen to live in might hold a terrorist or a murderer. They hate to think they have made a mistake about relocating here. It's understandable! I'd hate to find something awful had happened on *my* doorstep, or in *my* neighbourhood. But if we ask ourselves what is the worst of it, we will discover that it is the feeling of having been proved wrong, of having made a mistake.

Having looked at these examples as if they were about a friend, let's now imagine we were making these statements. If we take our first example of the person who retains a poor opinion of their ex- partner and analyse it more closely we can begin to see how that belief started.

It is hardly surprising that if, when we were having a very hard time with someone in our past, and we justifiably formed a strong negative definition of them, we are not wanting to see that maybe they are not so bad after all. We don't want to have to face the uncomfortable feeling that perhaps we were wrong. Maybe they aren't the totally negative person we made them out to be. "It takes two to tango" and it could be we were not being an angel at the time either! Perhaps we were both under stress, and neither of us was behaving like rational mature adults. It is no surprise that we choose to only see what we want to see, or hear only what we want to hear.

Continuing with our example, if someone is telling us about how kind our ex has been to an ill friend, we will dismiss their comments as being out of character, and then go on to put this piece of information out of our minds. However if the same person had told us something bad our ex had done, we would we more likely to get into a long discussion on all his shortcomings, and then add this new information to our already bulging arsenal against him! And why? Because the first one made us feel threatened and uncomfortable because our existing belief was challenged. The second reinforced our already existing belief.

Looking at our second and forth examples together, if we believe that our background or even a traumatic incident or loss has ruined our life, and all our personal failings are a direct result of this happening to us, we don't want to be reminded that others in a similar position, as the song says "stand themselves up, brush themselves down and start all over again!" It fits in with our beliefs to hold tightly to the victim stance. Being a victim definitely appears to have its benefits.

Firstly we have a wonderful reason not to have to take responsibility for what we are attracting to us. It's great when we can blame all our ills on someone or something else! It makes us feel sure of ourselves. The universe is known, understood! But at what cost to ourselves? Of course, we will not be put up for promotion, or attract happy, healthy people into our lives if we are constantly blaming other people for all our ills.

Also our beliefs tend to reinforce themselves, because the negative belief attracts more negativity to us for one simple reason. The universe reflects back to us what we tell ourselves about it! If we think it's a lovely benign place, quite often it will prove us right, by good things happening to us. If on the other hand we believe nothing we do ever works, nothing *will* ever work, because our belief is proving us right by only attracting negative situations and people to us.

We are so much more powerful than we think we are! Our thoughts and beliefs carry the power to transform our reality. Taking those first baby steps out of victim-hood, and back into the adult world is never easy. However as we begin to understand that on at least some level we do create our own reality, we become more willing to take these steps. This exercise can help us to move on.

Changing Limiting Beliefs

This is an N.L.P. exercise, and is quite complicated so I will explain it by giving an example of how it works. Neuro Linguistic Programming (NLP) is a wonderful system started over 30 years ago in America by John Grindler and Richard Bandler. It simply means re-programming the neurons or nerve pathways in our brain by changing the language we habitually use.

We can't even start the exercise until we can see in our own mind that the belief is indeed limiting, and possibly even erroneous. So this exercise will only help if you are already able to say that although you always used to believe it, you can now see it is not necessarily still true. What is more you are becoming aware of how this belief, plus the feelings that go with it are in fact holding you back and it is time to move on.

We can do the exercise with the third of our examples of limiting beliefs.

What is the Belief?	My sister is the clever one in our family
What is the Feeling?	Inferiority, stuck, useless

Take a Time Line back to the original memory

This means imagining yourself going up and out of the top of your head, and connecting to a line running back through your history, to the very first time you decided this was true. You can view your younger self in this situation, as if it was happening to some-one else and you are simply observing it on a screen. This way you never have to get caught up with the emotions of it. You are not reliving the memory, but are merely a detached observer. From this angle it is easier to see others' points of view as being just as relevant as your own, thus getting a totally fresh overview of the whole situation. In this case the person involved may see an incident in childhood where their big sister appeared to get preferential treatment, for example being encouraged to enter a writing competition, while the person in question was discouraged from entering it.

What was the good intention of everyone present?

Parents: To encourage big sister to do her best

To protect me from disappointment

Big sister: To do her best

Me: To prove I could do as well as my sister thus making me feel good about myself

Notice that we are willing to take the enormous leap of faith and believe that contrary to all indications that the opposite was true; deep in their hearts everyone does have good intentions, even if it is only to do something that will make them feel better, quite often at our expense! However, to see that in *their* mind, at that time, it was a good intention to them.

What was the good outcome for me?

I concentrated on my painting skills and ended up with a job I absolutely loved as an illustrator.

Again this is not always easy to answer, but if we are willing to see something good comes out of everything, then we are able to start to look for it and find it. It may be that the person in our example stopped their job when they had children or relocated and have therefore forgotten the fun they had working as an illustrator. And what they remember more than the fun job, was the on-going sense of being inferior to their sister, which is constantly being reinforced, despite the fact that maybe the sister is in such a high powered job she is totally stressed and unhappy! Spending time taking a serious look at this new information then enables us to answer the next questions.

Where is the Limiting Belief?   Gone

Where is the Limiting Feeling?   Gone

New Belief

Even though my sister may be more academically brilliant than me, I have in fact had a happier life. So obviously I am clever in a different way and I can start to appreciate and enjoy being me!

Having seen how this exercise works, now try asking yourself what is one of your limiting beliefs, and what are the limiting feelings that accompany it? But before attempting the above exercise for yourself, first of all ask yourself, "Am I willing to go through the initial discomfort of letting go of this long held belief?"

If the answer is "yes", then the truly million dollar question has to be "And am I willing to watch my life change for the better as a result of letting go of this belief?"

Happy Changing! Happy New Life!

Exercise Three

Changing Limiting Beliefs

1. What is the Belief?

2. What is the Feeling?

3. Take a Time Line back to the original memory

4. What was the good intention of everyone present?

5. What was the good outcome for me?

6. Where is the Limiting Belief?

7. Where is the Limiting Feeling?

8. New Belief

See References No.3 **Neuro Linguistic Programming**
en.wikipedia.org/wiki/Neuro-linguistic_programming
or contact Emma Mary Gathergood NLP Practitioner
emmamarygathergood@ymail.com

Chapter Four

Body Mind Awareness

Body Mind Awareness is based on the work of some of the best scientific and medical minds on the planet at this time. They include Candace Pert, a scientist who wrote "Molecules of Emotion" about the way our emotions leave an indelible stamp on the molecules in our physical nervous system; Deepak Chopra and Bruce Lipton who have both written books on the interconnection between body and mind; Herbert Benson, who back in the 1970s was the first person to teach "The Relaxation Response", a physical relaxation routine which helped to calm the mind as well as relaxing the body; Joe Griffin and Ivan Tyrrell who wrote a book called "Human Givens – a new approach to emotional health and clear thinking" which has been described as "an entirely attainable and reasonable road map for good mental health" by the Irish Examiner; and also Dr. David Mickel and John Eaton who founded "Reverse Therapy", another physical relaxation that works holistically, and which is described in more detail in this chapter.

What all these great modern scientists, doctors, philosophers and thinkers have in common is their awareness of the deep two-way link between our mind and our body. It appears that our body has its own intelligence and awareness and is not just an automated machine.

Fifty years ago all our scientific thinking was based on this reductionist theory, where everything was reduced to its smallest molecule, but little thought was given to the overall view and the connection between things. It is this rather arrogant belief system that has led to many of the problems we face in the world today, from environmental to health, from financial to global problems. This new way of looking at the world is much more inclusive, aware, open minded and forward thinking. Some of this new research has shown that our deepest emotions arise spontaneously from within and, in order to remain healthy, need to be expressed.

When these "e-motions" or energy-in- motion (as human emotions are described by Candace Pert) are suppressed, blocked or denied over time they enter into our physical cells, altering the functioning of these cells, and eventually causing severe damage to the hypothalamus in the brain. This results, after prolonged denial of the problem, in a breakdown of our health either physical, mental or both. When our glands are overstressed we begin to feel we simply can't cope any more. We become stressed, anxious, developing panic attacks, depression or the debilitating signs of Chronic Fatigue Syndrome. One of the new healing methods devised over the last few years is called Reverse Therapy. It teaches you how to re-connect to your own Inner

Healing Source, to be found within your own Body, thus allowing you to HEAL YOURSELF.

Imagine a therapy called Reverse Therapy - how perverse is that? Perverse maybe, but stunningly effective! Dr. John Eaton certainly knew what he was talking about when he named his new therapy "Reverse Therapy". So what was his intention? To reverse, not only the symptoms of exhaustion, anxiety and general malaise that cause M.E. but also to reverse the lifelong habits that led to this debilitating disease in the first place.

However the most unusual part of the *reversing* that happens in this therapy is that it reverses the trend of so many modern therapies to analyse, dissect and over-emphasise the thinking process. Reverse Therapy is in fact not about thinking at all, which according to Dr. Eaton comes from "Headmind" whereas the cure for this type of illness lies in "Bodymind", or the natural intelligence that is held in the cells of our body, and is more instinctive and immediate.

M.E. or Chronic Fatigue Syndrome affects at least 5% of the population at some time in their life. It often starts off with several nasty flu-type virus infections, which don't respond to antibiotics. Reverse Therapy teaches us that our symptoms are not our enemy, and therefore need to be eliminated. In fact the *reverse is* true. Our symptoms are actually our friends who have come to give us a message, and our job is to listen to them!

Instead of asking their clients to talk *about* how they are feeling or thinking, the Reverse Therapist asks the client to *sense* what is happening in their body, starting with concentrating on their feet. This concentration on sensation has the effect of allowing the body to begin to relax deeply, entering what they call Bodymind. The therapist is then able to enter into a dialogue with the body's own intelligence, and ask it some very probing questions.

Bodymind usually answers with some very telling and aware comments, which can come as a total surprise to the client, who usually has no idea that their body had the answers all along. These answers can then be interpreted by the therapist to work out what is the message the unpleasant symptoms have come to tell the client. This way of working certainly seem to point to the body's own innate capacity to heal itself, if only we will ask the right questions, then listen to the answers we receive. So the gist of the thinking behind Reverse Therapy is to reverse the trend of letting our mind dictate our behaviour, and instead learn how to listen to, and live by the wisdom of our Bodymind.

Several years ago I had to take early retirement due to Chronic Fatigue Syndrome. I was lucky enough to hear of the work of Dr Eaton in London, and his colleague Dr. Mickel, based in Scotland, whose Mickel Therapy works along similar lines. I saw a local Reverse Therapist, and after a number of sessions had improved to such an extent I was able to return to work on a part-time basis. So I am personally able to state the fact that with my therapist's help I was able to get in touch with the healing message my symptoms had come to tell me.

In my case this was a misuse of my energy, through allowing my mind to dictate what I should do, and for how long, instead of listening to my body's innate inner wisdom, which was more aware of my limits. Once I began to listen to the messages my body was sending me, it was only too willing to guide me as to when I needed to stop and rest. Up until that point in my life I had the sort of mind that dictated my actions, with very little awareness of my age, stamina, or paying attention to the little niggles and aches and pains that my body was using to attempt to get my attention, and let me know that all was not well.

I was reminded of the arrogance of too much mind-dominated thinking, realising what little regard our minds sometimes have for our bodies, or even our emotions. How often do we force ourselves to do something that just doesn't feel right, usually with disastrous consequences? Only when we think back can we see that our bodies may have been trying to get our attention through some unpleasant symptom, but we chose to ignore it, take a painkiller and carry on regardless! Or our emotions tried to attract our attention through anxiousness or low mood, but instead of spending time asking ourselves what this low mood was about, we gave ourselves a "talking to" and continued with the action that our low mood or anxiety was warning us against.

The more I have learnt to honour my body's innate wisdom, and the true nature of my emotions, I am much more physically healthy and I seldom get myself into those sticky situations, that I wish I hadn't started. Now, whenever I am in an unexpected low mood, or feel particularly uncomfortable or anxious about something I take time out to find out what is bothering me, and then take appropriate action.

Exercise Four

Connecting to Body Mind

Take some time to sit comfortably in a quiet place where you won't be disturbed for a while, and start to relax. Take a few deep breaths, and just as in Exercise One, begin to concentrate on relaxing your body. But this time having completed the full body relaxation, return to your feet. Really connect to how your feet feel in relationship to the ground beneath them, SENSE each different toe in turn, telling yourself what each toe can feel around it.

For example you may be saying something like this to yourself "Yes, I can sense the big toe on my right foot, I can feel its nail touching my sock, I can feel the bottom of it pressed on to the floor. I can feel its right side against my second toe, but I can't at the moment feel anything on its outer edge. Now, my second toe I can't feel at all... oh yes ....I can just feel it pressing against my big toe...."

You continue describing each sensation or lack of sensation to yourself in detail in a slow leisurely way. Then go on to sense the ball of your foot, your instep, your heel and ankle.

When you have completed the first foot, ask yourself if you can feel the difference between the two feet. You will begin to be aware the right foot is now warmer and feels heavier. This is because you are literally more IN your right foot than you are in your left, because of the few minutes you have just spent exclusively concentrating on it. Then move on to your left foot. Take about ten minutes to do this exercise, as this concentration on how your feet actually feel, allows you to become more grounded in your body, and so to come more easily into awareness of your Body Mind.

Then ask this sense of bodily awareness a question about any unpleasant symptoms you may have been experiencing. Ask what have these symptoms come to tell you. Don't allow yourself to go back up into your head, to think out an answer. Remain in the same place of sensing your feet, remaining completely relaxed and literally deeply grounded in your feet and legs and allow an answer to form itself. In this place of bodily awareness you are much more connected to sensation rather than thinking, you may get a total surprise as suddenly a fully formed answer appears, and you are aware you really didn't think up this answer. You will know the difference because the Body Mind answer will not be anything you have ever thought of before. It won't be part of your normal thinking pattern.

If this doesn't happen, don't worry, it may take some practice before you are able to converse with your body's innate intelligence in this way. However there is another way you can see if your Body will speak to you. Get pen and paper or write this exercise in your Journal. With your normal writing hand, begin to write the question, for example what is the message behind your symptoms. Then transfer the pen into your non-dominant hand, relax deeply into Body Mind, as in the previous exercise and begin to write out an answer. Because you are writing with your non-dominant hand it will be painfully slow, very much of a scrawl, but will in fact be capable of producing some quite surprising truths. Just relax and watch to see what information your body is willing to impart in this manner. You may well be very pleasantly surprised!

See References No.4

Dr. Eaton

The Wholistic Medical Centre

57 Harley Street, London W1G 8QS

www.reverse-therapy.com

Chapter Five

Solution-Focused Therapy and Positive Psychology

Something very exiting is happening! The most learned and senior spiritual leader in the world, the Dalai Lama, plus the ex-president of the American Psychological Association agree about something! And that is the need for us all to learn "The Art of Happiness". In his book of this name, the Dalai Lama says how shocked he was when first travelling in the west to discover the extent of depression and anxiety in the western world. Apparently, in his culture, people would seldom dislike themselves or have low self-esteem, despite their lack of material prosperity.

This points to a very interesting phenomenon. Possessions and riches do not necessarily bring happiness. In over forty years of working in the field of mental health, I am often surprised to find the extent of low self-esteem and personal dislike amongst the most attractive people, the extent of perpetual sadness in the wealthy, and the extent of anxiety and worry amongst the people with comparatively stress-free lives. This is obviously not what you would expect to find, and is an indication that these mental health problems are more to do with an inner malaise than an outer one.

Prior to the last ten years both depression and anxiety were seen as merely a chemical imbalance in the brain, to be healed with medication. However this has not been entirely successful. It has alleviated the worst of the symptoms, but it has not looked at the underlying issues that have caused the illness in the first place. Often the client has returned to normal life after a few months on antidepressants, but invariably within a few years there is a relapse. For this reason many psychiatrists at the leading edge of their profession have started looking beyond medication for a more lasting cure.

This is part of the situation we were discussing in the last chapter, about the old theories being superseded by more aware and enlightened thinking. As the connection between the body, mind, spirit and emotions is seen and understood more clearly, it becomes obvious that a purely chemical or bodily cure could never totally heal an illness that affects all four aspects of our being. The new holistic approach to medicine of all kinds is now willing to admit what Carl Jung was saying a hundred years ago which is that humans are made up of four aspects: body, mind, emotions and spirit.

The word "spirit" conjures up different things to different people. To some it is about all things irrational and unscientific. Now, when we consider purely reductionist science, as practiced up until the last few years, this belief was understandable. However now more and more physicists, doctors, psychologists and thinkers are accepting the holistic paradigm for the simple reason it offers successful treatment for illnesses, and an awareness that makes more sense and answers more questions than the old world view.

What *I* mean by spirit in the context of working to alleviate mental health problems, is finding that part of ourselves we discovered in the first exercise. That is the Detached Observer Self, or Aware Self, which when we are able to experience it, offers a sense of deep peace, relaxation, an inner knowing and a place of calm and safety.

Returning to our opening statement in this chapter, something unusual is indeed happening. Not only is the Dalai Lama talking about the need to find happiness, but so is the ex-president of the American Psychological Association, Professor Dr. Martin E.P.Seligman, who has written a book called Positive Psychology. He says that after more than 50 years of psychiatrists getting their depressed patients to talk about all the things that are wrong with their lives both now and in the past, there is no evidence to prove that this works to make them feel happier.

Solution Focused Brief Therapy

There are also other theories which agree with Positive Psychology, for example Solution Focused Brief Therapy, which encourages clients to spend at least half of the therapeutic session talking about what actually went **right** in their lives since the last session. This approach reinforces what we were discussing in Chapter 3, about how our beliefs and what we spend time thinking about affects how we experience the world. When a client leaves a session having spent the last half an hour talking about his successes, however minor, he is more likely to continue thinking about how well he is doing as he returns home. This in turn will encourage him to concentrate on the good things that *are* happening in his life, and lift his mood sufficiently for him to start to take positive steps towards creating a better life for himself in the future.

Positive Psychology

Returning to Positive Psychology, Dr. Seligman talks at length about the difference between the happiness generated by a pleasurable activity and the happiness generated from using your finest strengths and aptitudes. This is deeper, more long lasting and more authentic. He says there are three ways to live a happy life, the Pleasant, the Good and the Meaningful Life.

The Pleasant Life means understanding pleasure, and is experienced by participating in a pleasurable activity.

However he states that this type of pleasure can quite quickly turn sour as it is both shallow and difficult to maintain.

The Good Life means understanding gratification. It includes feeling challenged and acquiring skills. It requires concentration, clear goals and a sense of control. We find our sense of self vanishes, time stops and we are "in the flow". The Good Life consists of living a life where you are able to use your strengths and aptitudes in all areas of your life - work, relationships, family life, interests, hobbies and community.

Positive Psychology emphasizes the need to work with your best traits and strengths, rather than spend all your energy trying to develop the ones you fall short on. Enjoy and make the most of what you have, celebrating your strengths and accepting your weaknesses. The Good Life is both fulfilling and enjoyable.

The Meaningful Life, Positive Psychology declares, means connecting to the holistic nature of life. It consists of all the above plus connecting your life to something greater, to a purpose, either secular, spiritual or both. There are many ways of experiencing this. I feel it when sitting by a wild and raging sea; my second son, a sports journalist, feels it when at a football match and the crowd goes wild with joy when his side scores a goal; my eldest son, an installation artist, feels it when he successfully completes a major project; my daughter experienced it dancing at raves but also when her baby son first made eye contact with her; my father felt it in his beloved garden and my mother used to feel it when singing hymns. We tune in to the Meaningful Life whenever we experience being connected to something greater than ourselves.

See References No.5
Positive Psychology
www.positivepsychology.org.uk

Exercise Five

Discovering Positive Psychology

- List six activities that give you pleasure

- Recall a pleasurable activity you engaged in recently. Recall the afterglow and describe it briefly. How long did the afterglow last?

- What are your best qualities and strengths? How would a friend describe your most positive traits?

- Recall a recent activity that used some of your best strengths and aptitudes.

- Recall the afterglow and how long it lasted

- Recall a time when you felt really connected to either nature or other people or your own creativity. See if you can describe the feelings, thoughts and sensations associated with this experience in your Journal. Can you take steps to experience something like this again?

- Can you affirm to yourself that during this last experience you were totally connected to your Aware Self, the Truth of who you are, and as such, this experience can be replicated whenever you wish? The more you are able to let go of all the false beliefs and attitudes picked up throughout your life, and relax back into your True Self, as discovered in the preceding exercises, the more you can experience this deep sense of connection and joy, which is your true nature.

Chapter Six

C.B.T. and Coping Strategies

C.B.T. stands for Cognitive Behavioural Therapy, and the National Institute for Health and Clinical Excellence (NICE) guidelines now state it is the therapy of choice for both depression and anxiety. As the name implies CBT is a therapy that works with both how we think (Cognitive) and what we do (Behaviour).

It helps us to better understand how we think about ourselves, other people and the world in general. It also shows us how what we do affects our thoughts and feelings, just as how we think affects what we do. It can help us to change how we think, and what we do in order to feel better. It focuses on working with the present and the current problems we are experiencing, rather than concentrating on our past history and early life experiences.

Obviously sometimes we need to share some of our history in order for our therapist to understand where we are coming from, but most of the work concentrates on finding ways to improve our state of mind at the present time. There are many self-help books available now, where we can learn the basics, but sometimes it is helpful to talk to someone else.

In most parts of the country CBT is available on the NHS, and can be found by requesting a referral through our GP.

Challenge Negative Thinking

Over the years we tend to think along similar lines unless something or someone challenges this way of thinking. Often the way we think is not so much a conscious choice as a habit, either picked up from our family in childhood or slowly developed in adult life, often from our culture and our peers. We seldom stop to think if the way we approach life truly reflects our deep held values, beliefs and understandings. In order to move forward, CBT suggests we challenge our most negative thoughts, asking if they are really true, or just a habitual way of thinking.

Do we really believe we don't stand a chance, or that we must be perfect, that the world owes us a living or that we are worthless? Often these thinking patterns have become well-worn grooves in our brain from constant use and repetition. However when we start to analyse our thoughts, and ask ourselves if we really believe these negative thoughts, we have to agree, no, of course we don't.

Reducing Problems to Manageable Chunks

When our problems seem totally overwhelming it is often helpful to try to break them down into smaller segments, in order to find which segment we can start to change. The first segment is always the situation we find ourselves in. However it is closely followed by our thoughts, feelings, physical sensations, and actions. How we think about the situation will affect how we feel emotionally in terms of fear, sadness, frustration, anger and how we feel physically in terms of tension, exhaustion, anxiety, stress. These feelings affect what we do about it.

For example the diagram below shows how, if we view a situation as overwhelming, we will feel restricted in what we think we can do about it. But if we are able to learn some new coping strategies, the situation is no longer seen as overwhelming.

LARGE PROBLEM   +   FEW COPING STRATEGIES   =   **OVERWHELM**

However

LARGE PROBLEM   +   **NEW COPING STRATEGIES**   =   **ABILITY TO COPE**

As we can see the problem has remained the same size, but the increase in the size of coping strategies, has meant we are able to move from overwhelm to having a new found ability to cope. So let's look at some possible new coping strategies we could learn. Often situations seem overwhelming if we are faced with a new problem when we already feel we have enough to cope with, or when we are feeling particularly inadequate.

Examples of Coping Strategies

1. Use a skill learnt in Positive Psychology and remember a time when we had a major problem but overcame it. Remind ourselves that we *have* coped with difficult situations in the past and are stronger than we are currently feeling.

2. Decide to act a little more assertively. We will discuss this further in the next chapter, but for now let's ask ourselves if others are taking advantage of us, and is it time to put our foot down?

3. Alternatively are we wasting precious energy on ranting and raving about how everyone else is behaving, and focusing on blaming others rather than taking time out to look at what it is *we* are doing that could be exacerbating the problem? We will look more at this in the chapter on Anger Management.

4. Are we focusing on the negative and unnecessarily scaring ourselves with worst case scenarios, and catastrophic thinking? This is a common practice when we are feeling anxious, but once we realise the chances of these terrible outcomes happening are actually pretty remote, we can focus on more positive outcomes.

5. Ask ourselves what a capable friend or colleague would do in a similar situation, and then affirm that we too can develop the same skills they have. Look closely at how this person copes with life and start to model their behaviour. By acting how a successful person acts, we can soon begin to feel more successful ourselves. This is another NLP strategy and is a remarkably efficient way of learning a new skill.

6. Take this idea further and try asking for advice from well-intentioned friends who have our best interests at heart. However it is important that we never follow advice if it doesn't sit comfortably with us, or seems inappropriate or wrong to us.

7. Are we feeling less able to cope because we are tired or run down? Ensure that we have a good night's sleep before attempting to tackle a difficult problem. We also need to pay extra attention to maintaining a healthy diet during periods of stress, and take adequate exercise. Quite often a solution pops into our head while we are walking the dog!

8. We can do something completely unrelated to the problem to raise our self-esteem. Thinking back to the previous chapter, what are some of our strengths and virtues? What gives us joy and makes us feel connected? We can do something we know will lift our spirits, then approach our problem from the new perspective that this enjoyable experience brings.

9. Let's learn to nurture ourselves in whatever way works for us, a long hot bubble bath with soothing music in the background, a massage, a drink with a friend, or a day by the sea or in the woods.

10. And last, but by no means least, we can go back to any of previous exercises in this book, where we learnt how to connect with our Aware Inner Self which is always calm and at peace. If, as been suggested previously we are now making a habit of spending a few minutes a day connecting to this deep and healing part of ourselves, it will eventually become our first port of call in a crisis. We will begin to realise that there is always another way of looking at things, and perhaps this is not such a crisis after all, but instead an opportunity for us to practise spreading our wings and becoming the butterfly of our dreams!

Exercise Six

Discovering how our Thoughts affect our Feelings and Behaviour

Before doing this exercise let's take a look at how it works. We have already discussed how our thoughts affect our feelings, which in turn affects our behaviour, so we can now look at an example of this-

Situation--->	Thoughts--->	Feelings--->	Behaviour
We wake up to find it is raining	"Oh no! It's not raining again!"	Fed up, depressed	Pull the covers up over our head and stay in bed.

Possible change in our thoughts and how it affects what we do

We wake up to find it is raining	"Oh good! I won't have to water the garden, I can get on with ...."	Quite cheerful and up beat	Get up and start doing jobs in the house or reading a book

Example 2

Situation--->	Thoughts--->	Feelings--->	Behaviour
A friend cancels a pre-arranged date with us	"Oh dear, I knew she would let me down"	Hurt and upset, victim stance	Mope about at home being sorry for self

Possible change we could make

Situation	Thoughts	Feelings	Behaviour
A friend cancels a pre-arranged date with us	"I suppose she is a very busy person but it's ok, I can cope"	Determined this disappointing situation won't spoil our day	Phone another friend, and invite her along instead or decide to do something else

See References No.6

Cognitive Behavioural Therapy
www.nhs.uk and search for CBT

Exercise Six

Discovering how our Thoughts affect our Feelings and Behaviour

Now take a difficult situation that has recently happened to you and write down how you responded. Then make use of some of the coping strategies from the examples given above and then try looking at what else you could have thought instead, and how that would have affected how you felt and what you did. Remind yourself you are more able than you thought.

Situation--->	Thoughts--->	Feelings --->	Behaviour

Possible change in our thoughts and how it affects what we do. Perhaps try different strategies.

(Same situation)			

Chapter Seven

Mindfulness

Mindfulness originated as an ancient art of mind control practised by the Buddhist monks of Tibet and Thailand for thousands of years. However over the last 25 years Jon Kabat-Zinn, a psychotherapist from the University of Massachusetts Medical Centre and his colleagues developed a group programme, based on the same principles, for people suffering from both mental and physical health problems which they called Mindfulness-based Stress Reduction.

This programme teaches its clients how to overcome extreme levels of stress caused by either prolonged and severe physical pain, or debilitating levels of anxiety or depression by becoming mindful or aware of whatever is happening in their experience moment to moment. By paying deliberate attention to what is going on in their mind, body, feelings and experience, totally without judgement or self-criticism, these clients find unexpected benefits. Often a situation is exacerbated by worry about how much worse it might get.

Most of us find that by sitting quietly and monitoring what is actually going on, rather than focusing on what we fear might go on in the future, stress levels are reduced. Also this quiet contemplative attitude often allows new positive ideas about how to handle the problem to surface, and be thought about, instead of the tired old habitual response that was there in the past. New inner strengths and unexpected avenues of help are also more likely to present themselves to a quiet mind than a racing, stressed one. As long as we are thinking about wanting things to be different, we are not looking at what is actually good in our lives at this moment. This is a similar approach to the Solution Focused Therapy discussed earlier, but Mindfulness is more to do with training ourselves how to do a daily practice which gives us a new skill and a new approach to life, rather than a therapy to be administered by the therapist to the client.

The programme, started in America, has now spread to many other countries including England and Wales. The Centre for Mindfulness at Bangor University runs courses where therapists can train, and now it is possible to request to join a Mindfulness-based group on the NHS. Mindfulness-based approaches teach practical skills that are designed to help with daily challenges due to many health problems. Although the idea originated from Buddhism, nowadays they are taught in a totally non-religious context.

As well as the stress reduction programme, the mindfulness ideas have joined forces with the cognitive behavioural therapy discussed in the last chapter, to produce Mindfulness Based Cognitive Therapy. This is taught in an eight week programme and was developed for recurrently depressive clients, to be used when not in an acute stage, to learn to disengage from unhelpful mind sets which habitually result in further depressive episodes. These mind sets are characterised by obsessive rumination, where the mind reruns negative thoughts, memories and expectations, in a self-fulfilling prophecy of depressive outcomes.

The core skill learnt is to literally change gear. So instead of focusing on the repeated negative patterns, the focus is on becoming more aware of physical sensations, thoughts and feelings as actual mental events as they occur moment to moment. When seen in this way, it is possible to notice the transient nature of thoughts, feelings and sensations. Left to their own devices these experiences come and go, but are not cast in stone. It is only our attitude to them that can remain fixed and therefore cement them in place as if they were actual truths.

For example, following a loss or bereavement, if we watch our experience we can move through it and out the other side more easily. I put this to the test myself, in 2009 following the death of my beloved brother. When feeling overwhelmed with sadness I would sit quietly and concentrate on my breathing, as taught by MBCT, (Mindfulness Based Cognitive Therapy). Then I would become aware of the tension in my body, mainly a knot in my stomach. Again as I quietly breathed into this knot I would become aware with each subsequent breath, of my stomach starting to relax. I wasn't doing these changes, they were simply happening as I breathed into them.

Then I would become aware of sobbing, and again without judging I would watch the sobbing, breathing into the overwhelming feeling of loss. I tried repeating to myself, "Just watch the feeling of sadness, everything is all right, it's OK to be sad". This sort of reassuring self-talk obviously stopped the negative "I'll never get over this" type of thinking in its tracks. Although the aim of MBCT is not actually to stop the negative thinking, merely to become aware of it and watch it calmly until it moves into something else. By watching ourselves in this way and becoming aware of everything that is going on without judgment, the terrible sense of loss slowly lessens and after a while of practising this daily we become calmer and more at ease with our loss. We are still sad, but we are no longer overwhelmed by grief.

By working in this way, it allows us to have a healthier relationship to thoughts, feelings and sensations. We can see them as aspects of our experience, which are moving through our awareness in the moment. They are not our total reality. In other words, to quote from the Exercise in Chapter One, "I have these thoughts, feelings and sensations, but I am actually more than just them. I am an Aware Self, which is able to watch these experiences come and go."

The way this works is very similar to the experience of feeling better after having shared a negative experience with a friend. When we are thinking about it afterwards we cannot remember what the friend actually said, but what we do know is we feel better for having shared the experience. When we bring a mindful approach to bear on a problem we are experiencing, we actually are doing the same thing. We are sharing our difficult experience with our Aware Self, and as such end up feeling better, even though the outer problem hasn't changed. We feel better because our awareness is what has changed. We are no longer IDENTIFYING with the problem (I am very upset), but with our Aware Self (It is very sad that this has happened, but I am able to breathe into and let go of these strong feelings. I am able to cope with this and in time these overwhelming feelings will pass)

This is a very therapeutic experience for anyone who has had a long term diagnosis of depression and has come to see themselves as "a depressive". By regularly doing this mindfulness practice, this person will soon see they really are MORE than their depression and with this new awareness the whole depressive experience will change.

Exercise Seven

Experiencing Mindfulness

When you have a quiet half an hour you can decide to do some Mindfulness Practice. You can order a CD from The Mindfulness Centre at Bangor University, or you can join a group, but here is a simple meditative practice that can be done at home. Sit in a comfortable position, preferably in a straight backed chair, with your feet on the floor.

1. Concentrate on your breathing. Don't try to change it at all, just become aware of watching yourself breath in and out. Watch the speed, the depth and the quality of each breath, noting the space between the breaths too. Notice any changes that naturally occur in the breathing pattern as you watch it. After a few minutes move on to the next point.

2. Now concentrate on your bodily sensations. What part of your body is drawing your attention? Is that because it is uncomfortable? Ask yourself what sort of discomfort this is. Describe the sensations to yourself. Breathe into the sensations in a calm relaxed way. Just let them be. Even if somewhere is quite painful, note it is painful but without a value judgment, just breathe into the pain. As the

sensations change, notice the change and continue to breathe.

3. Become aware of your thoughts. Just watch them come and go in the same detached way you have just been experiencing your physical sensations. Realise that, like the sensations, they come and go. Become aware of not taking too much notice of each individual thought, believing it is the absolute truth. Understand our thoughts are just streams of consciousness, some sensible, some not! We don't need to listen to them all. Just watch them drift into and out of your mind, and start to become aware of the transient nature of thought. Reconnect to your breathing in a relaxed, calm way as you watch your thoughts come and go.

4. Now become aware of your feelings, watching them come and go in the same relaxed, detached way. If a feeling is particularly strong, breathe into the strong feeling, just allowing it to be how it is, with no judgment or criticism. Watch how it changes as you observe it.

5. Return to concentrating on your breathing and when you are ready, slowly stretch and yawn and return to whatever you were doing before you started the exercise. Note any difference in your overall sense of well-being.

The more you do this exercise the easier it becomes and the more benefit you will get out of it.

The key to its success is to be gentle with yourself, not berating yourself when your mind wanders, just gently bringing your mind back to the point, aware that you wandered off for a while. If you do it regularly, when you are really stressed or in pain you will find it is able to considerably reduce your stress levels, and improve your ability to cope in your day to day life.

See Reference No.7
Mindfulness Based Cognitive Therapy
www.mbct.co.uk
The Centre for Mindfulness Research and Practice,
School of Psychology
Bangor University, LL57 1UT

Part Two

Developing Assertiveness and Managing Anger

Chapter Eight

Understanding Assertiveness

So why is assertiveness important if we are trying to overcome depression and anxiety? It is important because so often we have become depressed because we have not really been expressing our needs, and maybe are feeling unheard or taken for granted. So often we are not being heard because we are not expressing our wants and needs clearly enough. Sometimes we are presuming that our loved ones SHOULD know what we want. This assumption only brings us pain, when our loved ones have their own agenda and are too preoccupied with getting their own needs met to be able to second guess what our needs are.

The first important premise about assertiveness is that we need to have respect for ourselves and others. That means we need to believe that our opinions, beliefs, thoughts and feelings are as important as those of someone else. When we value what we think and feel, have self-esteem and respect for ourselves, then we want to learn how to express ourselves as clearly as possible. In recognising our own strengths and limitations we need to be honest with ourselves about what we are thinking and feeling. It is important to take time to get in touch with our own wants and needs, and then be as honest as possible in our communication with others about those needs. To edit what we want to say in order to convey a certain impression, to protect others from hurt or to manipulate them into doing what we want is not being assertive.

Being assertive means taking responsibility for our life and our choices, making our own decisions, and not blaming other people or circumstances for our problems. Having been willing to take responsibility for attempting to resolve the problems in our life, we can start to make changes in order to make our life more the way we want it to be. If we blame outside circumstances it means we are helpless and a victim. It is both challenging and exciting to know we can become the creator of our own life. Ultimately we are responsible for what happens to us and that can become empowering and even fun.

Being assertive is also about being self-aware, looking at our own behaviour and possible ways of changing it, liking ourselves and not judging ourselves, in fact accepting ourselves the way we are right now. When we are assertive we are feeling confident about being able to create what we want.

Aggression is often confused with assertiveness, but needs to be seen as totally different. If we are being aggressive, we are putting our own needs above those of other people and pursuing them regardless of the effect on others. Acting aggressively is expressing feelings and opinions in a way that punishes, threatens or puts the other person down, disregarding the rights and needs of others, aiming to get our own way no matter what. Being aggressive might get our needs met but it does not make us feel good.

Passivity is at the opposite end of the scale. This is characterised by not standing up for our rights, allowing others to take advantage of us. Passivity is about avoiding responsibility for making choices, allowing others to make our decisions for us. When we are passive we might see ourselves as helpless victims of unfairness and injustice, or we get what we want indirectly by manipulation or game playing. Again this doesn't make us feel good.

Assertiveness takes the middle road. It is characterised by recognising our needs, and asking openly for what we want, plus recognising and respecting the rights and needs of other people. When we are being assertive we are relating to people in an open and honest way; feeling responsible for and in control of our own actions. We are prepared to compromise rather than insisting on winning or losing. **Being assertive makes us feel good!**

Bill of Rights

In 1975 Manuel J Smith's book "When I Say No, I Feel Guilty" proposed the concept of the Bill of Rights. The idea has been developed by many writers since. It aims to define some of the basic human rights that we all possess; indicating that we are **all** equal and that we **all** possess the same basic rights. It is essential to learn to **stand up for your rights without violating the rights of others.**

Here are some of our basic human rights:-

- ✓ I have the right to make my own choices, express my feelings, opinions and beliefs

- ✓ I have the right to say "yes" and "no" for myself, declining the requests of others.

- ✓ I have the right to have needs, desires and preferences and ask for help.

- ✓ I have the right to be listened to, taken seriously and treated with respect.

- ✓ I have the right to make mistakes and change my mind

Feel free to add any rights that you feel are important to you.

Exercise Eight

How Assertive are You?

How easy is it for you to be assertive in the following situations? Score 1-5, making 1 very easy and 5 very difficult.

➢ Expressing your feelings to someone

➢ Discussing your opinions with someone with a different opinion

➢ Receiving a compliment

➢ Having an argument with someone

➢ Refusing a request

➢ Asking for a favour

➢ Giving yourself a treat or doing something you may feel is selfish

➢ Admitting you don't know something

➢ Expressing anger directly

➢ Giving a talk or lecture

86 Developing Assertiveness and Managing Anger

➢ Telling someone you don't like what they are doing

➢ Saying "No" without making excuses or being overly apologetic

➢ Telling someone you really like them

➢ Giving a compliment

➢ Returning an article to a shop

➢ Starting a conversation with a stranger

If you have scored more than 45 you need to practice being more assertive. As you become more assertive watch to see how your self-worth and your mood improve.

Chapter Nine

Understanding Anger

Anger is primarily an emotion. Like all emotions, it is there to inform us about what is going on in our world. The positive emotions, such as joy, fulfilment, satisfaction and contentment are there to inform us we are experiencing something we like and would like more of. Equally the negative emotions, such as anger, hurt, fear, sadness, guilt, jealousy are there to inform us that all is *not* well in our world, and we are not comfortable with the present situation. This in turn lets us know we need to make some changes.

When we look at life like this we can begin to see that our negative emotions are extremely important to our well-being. How would we ever be in the position to make informed decisions if our negative emotions were not indicating what was amiss in our world? However sometimes we develop a liking for one emotion and a dislike of another, so we may become more comfortable expressing one emotion than another.

The problem with this inappropriate use, or over-use of one emotion to the exclusion of all other emotions, is that we cease to get a true picture of our world and our real feelings about it. So we become confused and stuck. Also if our preferred emotion is anger, not only are we stuck, but also our relationships become stuck.

Because anger is a rather unacceptable emotion in many households or working environments we may find ourselves getting blamed for everything that goes wrong. For example, someone may behave in a way that we feel is unacceptable towards us. Because anger is our first response, we become angry towards them. Before we know what is happening we are getting the blame for our anger outburst and the original bad behaviour is slipping by unnoticed. This, over time, infuriates us so much that our anger worsens, and a vicious circle is set in motion.

Anger can be used to block out more painful emotions such as anxiety, hurt, depression, guilt or shame, which are even more difficult to handle. Anger can also be used to dispel stressful physical sensations. These may include muscle tension, headaches, tiredness, indigestion or stomach cramps. Sometimes the anger outburst releases these symptoms and we feel physically more relaxed afterwards.

We can use anger to discharge feelings of stress when we are frustrated because our needs are not being met and may achieve more "arousal reduction" than other responses.

Arousal is when our heart is beating fast, we are flushed, perhaps shaking and feeling overwhelmed. An angry outburst can restore this arousal to more manageable proportions by quickly releasing the build-up of energy in our internal system.

Anger is also useful for dealing with a threat. It can give us the surge of energy we need to escape from, or turn and fight an aggressor. Anger may simply be a response, which comes more naturally to us than other responses. It may have been learnt in our childhood home as the norm for self-expression.

Dealing with Stress

In life it is impossible to exist without encountering stress in one form or another. We do not all find the same events stressful. In fact what is one person's stress is another's exhilaration or pleasure. However each of us finds certain things stressful, and our body, mind, emotions and spirit look for ways to eliminate this stressful arousal and return us to a more comfortable level of functioning.

Coping mechanisms consist of anything that increases our ability to cope, be this in the form of a physical workout or relaxation routine; a constructive reappraisal of the situation; a reassuring or calming thought; or a decision to view the situation from a totally different perspective.

However another form of coping mechanism despite being unhelpful, does actually work to reduce our stressful arousal in the moment, but is in fact a maladaptive response to stress.

This consists of various emotional outbursts, usually using the emotion which we are most used to experiencing and therefore most comfortable expressing. If fear is our usual response we may become anxious or experience panic attacks. If hurt and sadness is uppermost in our repertoire we will burst into tears. And if anger is our primary response we will quickly become angry and confrontational.

It is essential to realise that this is not in itself negative. In fact we most likely developed this reaction at a time when we were quite young. At this time, few creative responses to stress were either known to us or available to us at that time. The minority of us grew up in families where a normal reaction to stress was to do something positive and helpful. If our parents and teachers were unaware of successful coping mechanisms, it is hardly surprising that we grew up copying them in their maladaptive behaviour. They were our role models after all.

Triggers - Inner and Outer

Inner Triggers are anger-triggering thoughts. Examples of these thoughts are:

- seeing others as bad, wrong or deserving of punishment;

- blaming others

- believing others deliberately do nasty things to us, rather than they are simply preoccupied with their own problems and somewhat unaware of ours

- feeling others SHOULD have done ...

- seeing ourselves and our needs as being far more important than others and their needs

- thinking our belief systems and ideologies are superior to other people's and therefore we have a right to preach to them

External triggers are situations, events, behaviour or words of others. These can be situations or conversations that remind us of painful situations in the past, and so our anger is actually directed at the person from our past rather than the current situation. Or they could be events we find physically overwhelming as in prolonged loud noise, or physically painful experiences (as in someone treading on our toe).

They could be mentally challenging as in when we realise we actually don't really know as much about a subject as the person we are speaking to, or conversely we know considerably more, but the other person is convinced we know nothing! They may be emotionally challenging, as in affairs of the heart, jealousy or feeling betrayed, treated unfairly or let down. Or they may be spiritually challenging, as in disagreements of a political, religious or philosophical nature.

The Symptoms of Anger.

People have different symptoms but they all fall into three categories.

Physical:- our heart pounding; gritting our teeth; becoming red faced and hot under the collar; feeling our stomach knotting up; tension between our eyes; sweaty palms; our hands start to shake; a dry mouth or feeling our knees becoming weak.

Emotional:- feel like bursting into tears; feel frightened or like running away; feel out of control; energised; anxious; resentful; feel that it isn't fair or that we don't stand a chance, feeling violent and wanting to lash out or feel like saying hurtful, unkind things.

Behavioural:- raising our voice, shouting, swearing or using abusive language; starting to cry or be cutting or sarcastic; staring at the person in a threatening manner or refusing to use eye contact; raising our fist as if to hit them; wagging our finger in a dictatorial way; shouting them down or refusing to hear their point of view; withdrawing from them physically or actually using physical violence.

The End Result of Anger

We may end up feeling to blame, feeling exhausted or as if we lost the war, even if we won the fight; totally misunderstood or as if it was a storm in a teacup; wondering what just happened, or how on earth it started; it may spoil our relationships; interfere with our home or working life; exacerbate physical symptoms; happen too often; leave us feeling sad or that we still haven't got to the bottom of the problem.

Different Anger Styles

There are three main ways people deal with their anger. The first is to "stuff it" or to pretend you are not feeling what you are feeling. The second is to escalate it, making it grow into something larger and more intimidating than the original feeling. And the third way is to successfully manage your anger. Obviously the aim of looking at our anger is to learn how to manage it to the point where it is no longer a problem for us or others.

Stuffing our Anger:- this is when we attempt to deny to ourselves or others that we are angry; avoid or are uncomfortable with direct confrontation; or get a jittery tummy at the thought of having to tell someone we disagree with them.

Maybe anger reminds us of frightening times from childhood; or we feel guilty or ashamed of showing anger or feel it's not OK to be angry. Or perhaps we have difficulty coping with the strong emotion or intense reaction we may feel if we allow ourselves to experience anger; have a fear of losing control or feel we don't have a right to be angry. We may have a fear of hurting or offending someone or have a fear of being disliked, rejected or judged harshly. Maybe we were told as a child that it was wrong to be angry or were so put off by angry people in our childhood that we vowed to be different from them. The problem with stuffing our anger is that it usually comes out anyway and often in an indirect, manipulative or undermining way. So this anger style impairs relationships and compromises our physical and mental health.

Escalating our Anger:- to escalate, according to the Concise Oxford Dictionary, means to increase or develop by successive stages. So when we escalate our anger we increase it by successive stages. If we are a person who does this, it implies that at repeated stages of our outburst we continue to make the same choice, i.e. that what we want to do is keep getting angrier. It may be that we have never thought about this before, or if we have, felt that we had no choice about our increasing rage. Escalation is like climbing a flight of stairs where each step takes us nearer to the fire-breathing dragon that lives at the top - us in a full blown anger outburst!

When escalating our anger we may :- feel we have no other choice; feel that we have need to demonstrate our strength or power; get angry in an attempt to avoid expressing other underlying emotions; feel afraid of getting close to someone; feel anger is the only way we can get our feelings across. The problem with escalating anger is that the desired results may only be short lived. We may also cause physical destruction, impair relationships, and compromise both physical and mental health. If anger really escalates out of control there may also be damaging legal ramifications.

The best way to manage our anger is to accept it, get to know it, understand it and decide to make new choices. When we look at both the benefits and cost of our angry outbursts, then weigh them against the benefits and costs of managing our anger that will provide us with the motivation to change.

Before reading the rest of this chapter, go on to do Exercise Nine. Only when you have completed it, when you more readily understand your own anger style, signs and symptoms, then return to truly be able to……

Manage Your Anger

Are you now willing to begin to accept that your anger is not helping you to be loved, understood or supported? Indeed it is not helping you get any of your true needs met. So are you willing to decide to make some new choices? At each stage, from the low rumblings of discontent to the full explosion of your temper, you are free to backtrack or take time out to review what you are really feeling, rather than launching into the old automatic response.

If you don't want to become an automaton, decide to remain fully conscious at each stage, making new creative choices about how to respond. These may include repeating calming thoughts e.g. "I have nothing to prove" or "I don't need to take this personally", giving yourself time out by walking away or suggesting you discuss it later when you have time to reappraise the situation. It is often helpful to tell the other person you are feeling angry and wish to have time out to calm down before continuing.

Develop an ABC of Calm

Answer your opponent in a slow, quiet voice

Back off from them

Calm your body by relaxing your shoulders and

stomach muscles

Deepen and slow down your rate of breathing

Empathise with the other person, imagining how they are feeling right now

Fantasise about a calm, beautiful scene where you feel great

And finally congratulate yourself on your willingness to accept your anger, recognise its destructive influence, and be willing to let it go. Having removed yourself from the situation, allow the arousal feelings to reduce through physical exercise or relaxation. Try other techniques such as a Mindfulness Meditation, or any chosen occupation that you know may help, such as listening to music, dancing, relaxing in a bubble bath or reading something totally absorbing. What other creative ways of managing your anger can you discover?

Last of all do not blame either yourself or others for your anger, as it only escalates it further by making you feel worse. Learn to love and accept yourself with a non-judgemental attitude, knowing you are doing your best.

Exercise Nine

Getting to Know your Anger

The following exercise will help you to make different choices. Think about the last time you were angry. This may not be so easy if you are a person who stuffs their anger. However if this is so, try and think about a time when you suspect you may have been angry, but expressed your pent up emotions in a different way, for example crying or having a panic attack. Write down the whole experience from start to finish, and then try to answer these questions as honestly as possible.

- Anger can be used to block out more painful emotions such as anxiety, hurt, depression, guilt, and shame. What were you REALLY feeling?

- Anger can also be used to dispel stressful physical sensations. What were you experiencing physically before the anger kicked in? How can you start to express these feelings before you resort to anger?

- Anger can discharge feelings of stress when you are frustrated because your needs are not being met, or you are being forced by circumstances to do things you do not want to do. What needs of yours are not being met? Or what are you doing that you really don't want to have to do?

- Anger is also useful for dealing with a threat. It can give us the surge of energy we need to escape from, or turn and fight an aggressor. What in your life at this moment is posing a threat to you? The threat may constitute a fear of loss; an inability to set your own limits or boundaries; a feeling of being out of control; or feeling you don't have any rights or any chance to say "no".

- Anger may simply be a response, which comes more naturally to you than other responses. Has anger become your habitual response to many life situations?

- Anger may achieve more "arousal reduction" than other responses. Do you find you calm down quicker and return to an acceptable level of arousal faster if you can express your anger?

- Anger may also have been a conditioned response from childhood. Did you find, as a child, your "tantrums" were rewarded? Did your parents give in to your furious demands, so it became a way of getting heard and noticed?

- Anger may have been learnt in your childhood home as the norm for self-expression. Did everyone get very angry in your family, so you picked it up by imitating your parents or peers?

- Inner Triggers are anger-triggering thoughts. What sort of thoughts do you have that serve to escalate your anger? Are you aware of using SHOULD or OUGHT or MUST? Are you willing to change these thoughts?

- Also do you have some underlying beliefs about how others SHOULD behave, that need to be reviewed and moderated?

What are some of your external triggers? What situations appear to bring out your anger? Scoring 1-5, making 1 low level and 5 very high, rate your level of irritation or hostility to the following scenarios.

- Being treated unfairly

- Being treated cruelly

- Being made fun of

- Your family being criticised

- Being treated without respect

- Not being heard or listened to

- Being patronised or talked down to

- Your expertise being ignored

- Someone who doesn't know what they are talking about

- Being criticised

- Being lied to

If you have scored more than thirty, you DO have a problem with anger and need to start to manage it more successfully.

How could you react differently to the triggers that you scored the highest? Work out and write down a new coping strategy to try with each of these triggers. Decide to really start to change your blind automatic responses to something more aware and thought out. Practice these new responses at every opportunity.

Now think about these questions:

➢ How do you usually react to your feelings of anger?

➢ What factors often lead to this feeling?

> How do you express your anger non-verbally?

> What are the physical symptoms you have when you are angry?

> Do you get angry at the same people over and over again? If so, why?

> Do you use anger as a screen for other emotions?

Do you stuff your anger by:- attempting to deny to yourself or others that you are angry; avoiding or being uncomfortable with direct confrontation; get a jittery tummy at the thought of having to tell someone you disagree with them or become reminded of frightening times from childhood? If so, what are these memories?

> Were you made to feel guilty or ashamed if you showed anger as a child?

> Do you feel it's not OK to be angry or do you feel you don't have a right to be angry?

> Do you have difficulty coping with the strong emotion or intense reaction you may feel if you allow yourself to experience anger? Or you have a fear of losing control?

➢ Have you experienced this in the past and wish to avoid it at all costs?

➢ Do you have a fear of losing or damaging a relationship? Has this happened to you in the past or do you have a fear of being disliked, rejected or judged harshly?

➢ Were you told as a child that it was wrong to be angry? Do you still believe that?

➢ Or were you so put off angry people in your childhood that you vowed to be different from them?

If you answered "yes" to several of these questions it should be clear that this is your anger style. Give yourself permission to feel and express your angry feelings in a calm, clear, non-blaming way. Then, regardless of the reaction you get, congratulate yourself for expressing your anger, then let it go by exercising, doing a household chore, doing a Mindfulness Meditation or distracting yourself in any chosen enjoyable pursuit.

Or do you Escalate your Anger?

➢ Remembering a recent angry outburst. Did you feel you had no other choice than to be angry?

➢ Do you remember the exact course of events and what

you thought and said as you got angrier? List your statements or actions in chronological order e.g. 1-6

➢ Can you see that each stage paved the way for the next stage? Is there a link between successive statements?

➢ Could you have gone straight from no.1 to no.6?

➢ Can you imagine anything different that you could have said or done at each stage that would have de-escalate the situation?

Remember the fire-breathing dragon that lives at the top of the escalator, representing the angry you? In this last outburst did you feel that you had a need to demonstrate your strength or power?

o How else could this have been achieved?

o Did you feel anger was the *only* way you could get your feelings across?

o Is this true, or can you think of other ways?

o Is this a learned response? If so, it can be un-learned.

Now return to finish reading the chapter at page 96, and learn how best to MANAGE your anger.

Part Three

Overcoming Depression and Anxiety

Chapter Ten

Understanding Depression

When looking to understand our own depression it is very important to see that we are MORE than our depression. It may be that if we have felt depressed for a long time and been treated by our GP or the local psychiatric service, we have started to see ourselves as "a depressive". Instead of seeing ourselves as a person who at the moment is overwhelmed by depressive thoughts and feelings, we start to lose sight of ourselves as a person at all.

If you are feeling like that at the moment, just stop reading this chapter and re-read Chapter One, doing the exercise as described.

Are you able to see that however exhausted your body may be feeling; however negative your thoughts may be; and however low your feelings are, you, yourself, in your heart of hearts are MORE than any of these sensations, thoughts or feelings? You are, deep down inside you, an AWARE SELF, able to connect to the earth itself below you, and the heavens above you. As you sit for a while in contemplation of the vastness of the universe and your unique and sacred place within that whole, you can begin to sense the fact that you are part of the whole. And as such are linked through your humanity to everyone else on the planet.

As you spend time becoming aware of this Truth, you can also reconnect to the discussion in Chapter Two about the Three Faces of Self. At the moment, in your depressed state you may feel the **Outer Face You Show to the World** is not very good, neither is the **Face You Hide from the World**. Both are over laden with depression. But, as stated in Chapter Two neither of these are your True Self. Underneath both these depressive faces is the **Face of Who You Truly Are**, which is not depressed at all.

Think back to when you were last engrossed in a pleasurable occupation. Maybe you were gardening, cooking or listening to some lovely music, stroking a cat, or chatting to a loved one or enjoying lying in a warm, comfortable bed. Remember that sense of being part of the whole, of belonging to the wonderful web of all of Life. This is your True Self, and by thinking about this happy memory, you reconnect to your Inner Healer, who has the power to help you let go of your depressive thoughts and feelings.

I suggest you read through all the following suggestions before deciding on one or two that you resonate with, and start by working on those first.

Challenge Negative Thoughts

Looking back to Chapter Six about C.B.T., you can see how your thoughts affect your feelings which in turn affect your behaviour. What are some of those recent depressing thoughts? Try writing them down then challenge them. Are they strictly true? If your thoughts have recently been about how your "glass is half empty," then try changing them to "my glass is half full" type thoughts. For example if they have been about how awful life is at the moment, ask yourself what in your life is good. For example your health, your family, friends, the weather, the trees or birds outside your window, your favourite radio or TV programme, your full fridge or the fact we are not living in a war zone, nor are we wrongly imprisoned or starving to death.

Get Out of the Rut of Negativity

Over time, similar types of thoughts create a distinct neural pathway, from one set of neurones to another within the physiology of the brain. Imagine a tractor driving into a fresh green field after a lot of rain. As it drives through the field it sinks into the mud, leaving its mark. The next time he has to cross the field the driver thinks it is easier to follow the same tracks. Over the next few weeks, he doesn't even have to think, he just follows the groove. One day, when the ground is hard and solid with frost, there is a fallen tree in the path, but he is unable to steer his tractor on a new route, because the grooves of his well-worn path have become so deep and so solid it is impossible to move out of the self-created rut.

As we repeatedly think similar types of thoughts, the neural pathway in our brain becomes deepened into a rut, which then tends to make our thinking patterns stereotyped and automatic. If over the years we have become used to thinking in a depressive, negative way, we need to really make a decision to watch our thoughts, steering them in a new direction, if we wish to overcome our depression.

Look for the Good

As we begin to take responsibility for our thoughts, we can start to see we do have the power to pull ourselves out of depression with help. Maybe we have been feeling there is no help available just lately. The problem is, the more we dwell on this lack, the more the lack of help will present itself to us.

Try a little experiment. Think about what help IS available. List the various people who have helped you in however small a way in the last month, from the driver who stopped to let you cross the road, to the friendly lady in the Post Office, from the polite child next door who thanked you when you returned their ball to the tall gentleman in the supermarket who reached that jar from the top shelf for you!

Affirmations

Then write in your Journal in large letters "Help is available when I need it!" Also write this out several times, leaving little notes for yourself around the house. As you repeat this affirmation at least hourly to yourself, watch to see how things change over the next few days, and be sure to make a note in your Journal about the unexpected help that you draw to you. Simply by changing your belief about the level of help available will have changed your thinking process, which will allow more help into your life. You will be amazed at how this one small change can begin to attract to you a whole different set of circumstances.

Volunteering

Having thought about all the helpful people in your life, could you take it a stage further by thinking of all the people who could be in need of YOUR help. Could you offer to pick up the paper for the neighbour with a broken leg? Could you offer to collect a friend's child from school, or fetch a prescription for an elderly neighbour? Taking it a stage further, when you are feeling a little better, could you volunteer an hour a week in the local charity shop? The more you start to move towards making contact with others the more you realise that you are not alone. Many people feel just as isolated as you do and would welcome a friendly word or gesture from you. Once you have broken the ice by being friendly towards someone, you will be surprised how pleased they are to see you next time.

Participation

Another way to cheer yourself up is to participate in local events, from a coffee morning at the local church, to a free lunchtime concert. When people go to the effort of organising something, they are really grateful to you for participating. Imagine how frustrated they would feel if nobody came! There is always something or someone who would be glad to see us, if only we can make the decision to start to reconnect with others. When we are able to see we are MORE than our depression, we are able to start to take those first, tentative steps back into feeling we belong in our family and community and wanting to interact with them.

Become Your Own Best Friend

Having said all that do not spend so much time with others that they drain your energy and leave you feeling depleted. Work out how long it is reasonable to spend visiting a sick relative, excusing yourself before you feel exhausted. Then remember to congratulate yourself firstly for going, and secondly for looking after yourself sufficiently to know when to leave!

Sometimes we become depressed because we are being too hard on ourselves, so learn how to become your own very best friend, comforting yourself when you are down, supporting yourself in your decisions, and encouraging yourself when you are reticent. How would you like your loving caring friend to speak to you? Write down what you would like to hear, and then start to tell yourself these things. You will be amazed at how much better you feel when you become your own best friend.

Enjoyable Activities

So apart from helping others, what else used to give you joy? Make a list of every activity you have ever done that you really enjoyed, from going to a cookery class, to painting a picture, from dancing round the living room to your favourite CD to catching a train to the next town, from going to a talk on ancient history to visiting a friend with a baby. Having made your list, you could decide to do one of those things within the next week, remembering to give yourself lots of encouragement.

Create a Comfort Basket

Sometimes when we are feeling at our worst it is hard to think of something to cheer ourselves up. However if we have previously prepared a collection of some of our favourite things all together in one place, it is easier to just pick something out and use it to help us feel better.

So on a good day put together a Comfort Basket, which is simply a basket full of things that cheer you up, for example your favourite CD or DVD, some lovely smelling bubble bath, your favourite aromatherapy oil or scented candle, your favourite sweets, some photographs of a time in your life when you were happy, your favourite book of poems or short stories, a treasured ornament or keepsake, a comfy cushion or wrap, the phone number of a good friend and a list of helpful ideas, thoughts and affirmations that you have found useful in the past.

Then on a bad day enjoy indulging yourself, with these handpicked items that you chose for yourself with love. Feel the love!

Have an Early Night

Sometimes we are feeling depressed because we are simply over-tired. After a few bad nights or a stressful few days we may be in need of a good night's sleep. However if we are prone to depression, it is easy to blame our depression for our low mood, rather than seeing that exhaustion makes everyone feel down. So try distracting yourself by watching a favourite old movie, reading a good book or having an early night. Things usually look better in the morning light.

Use a Daily Relaxation Routine

Every day listen to a relaxation or meditation CD or do one of the exercises in this book. By making this part of your daily routine, it will be more effective when you use it on a bad day, and will help to keep you feeling connected and at peace.

Daily Exercise

Do at least twenty minutes exercise daily to keep yourself healthy and lift your mood. This can be a walk in the park, a jog round the block, dancing in your living room, or going to an exercise class. It could even be digging the garden or vacuuming, cleaning windows or mowing the lawn, it doesn't really matter as long as it gets your heart pumping and your blood circulating, because it is this that gets the endorphins flowing and lifts your mood.

Healthy Diet

Often when you are depressed you lose interest in food, however this becomes a vicious circle, because if you are not eating a healthy balanced diet your mood will suffer. Think back to the last time you enjoyed a meal. What were you eating?

Plan to go to the shops and buy yourself either this or something else you used to enjoy. Then come back and prepare it with love for yourself as if you were an honoured guest. Make the preparation and eating of this meal a special event that you have chosen to do to improve your mood. As you eat it tell yourself how good it feels to eat food cooked with love.

Decide to spoil yourself at least once a week, and begin to look forward to these special occasions. List all your good points and decide to celebrate your positive new opinion of yourself with a special meal. Enjoy the occasion!

Once you are enjoying food again it is good for both your mental and physical health to start to really plan a balanced diet with plenty of fresh fruits and vegetables, food that is alive and vibrating with life force, rather than processed food. Too much refined or sugary foods will dampen your newly developing sense of aliveness and wellbeing.

There are many books and articles on what defines a balanced diet so take a trip to the library and try to get interested in which foods make you feel better and which are best avoided. You could also visit an allergy specialist to see if some of your low mood is due to an allergic reaction to certain foods. However do not become obsessional about this, as that will be counterproductive to your efforts to lift your mood. After all, our thoughts affect our moods much more than our diet.

Create a Gratitude Journal

Buy a special new notebook, or start to work from the back of your daily journal. Every night, just before you put the light out, write down five things you are grateful for, and try not to repeat things you have written before. This is a wonderful way of concentrating your thoughts on the positive just before falling asleep. This worked very well for me. I first heard this idea on the Oprah Winfrey Show that used to be on the TV at lunch time. I was going through a particularly stressful time, and felt there was little in my life to be grateful for and lots to dislike! However I decided to give it a go and after a few weeks became aware of having a better night's sleep, less stressful dreams and waking up feeling more refreshed and able to face the day. It does seem that falling asleep with a positive thought in your head definitely affects the quality of your sleep and subsequently your mood on the following day.

Become Your Own Expert

Above are fourteen ideas for helping you to lift yourself out of depression. As suggested, find one or two that appeal to you and start working on those straight away. Then over the next few days and weeks start to attempt some of the other ideas, remembering to keep a note in your journal as to which ones work best for you.

In some parts of the country the NHS is starting up an Expert Patient Programme. It is designed to give long term sufferers of illnesses the chance to learn how best to manage their illness, thus allowing the patient, rather than the Doctor to become the expert on their condition. This is a very empowering experience for someone whose illness had led them to feel disempowered and often at the mercy of the so-called experts. If you have access to the internet you can look up to see if there is a programme in your area by typing in "NHS Expert Patient Programme". Or you can ask your GP about it, and possibly get involved, because if you do have a depressive illness, you really can become an expert on your illness and maybe able to pass on helpful tips to other sufferers of depression, which will in turn help you to feel better

Chapter Eleven

Understanding Anxiety and Panic Attacks

Anxiety can be the most debilitating of all mental health problems, because the body often joins in with the general heightened arousal and produces quite frightening sensations and actually on occasions, violent physical discomfort and pains. If we are unaware these are caused by stress and anxiety, we can believe we are having a serious health problem and even phone the emergency services, thinking we are dying! The best way to cope with this is firstly to learn a little about the body's natural and healthy response to stress.

The Fight or Flight Response

Supposing we were to look out of our window right now and see our neightbour's house on fire. What would we need in order to protect ourselves? Well we would obviously need to have the presence of mind and energy to either tackle the blaze or run away. So this is exactly what the body does when we have the thought that there is an emergency happening.

➢ The mind goes into "Red Alert", with heightened sensitivity. We go into survival mode, where our hearing suddenly becomes more acute, our eyesight more clear, our sense of smell increases, our tactile sense becomes more acute, all enabling us to make an instant decision to ensure our own safety.

➢ Adrenaline is released in our blood stream causing our heart to beat faster and we start to breathe faster and more shallowly in order to allow us to have more oxygen in our blood which will increase our energy levels.

➢ Our hands start to shake as the blood is directed away from the extremities to the large muscles in our legs to help us to run faster.

➢ We start to sweat profusely, which is nature's way of cooling us down after the exertion our bodies are expecting us to make at any minute.

➢ Our mouth goes dry, because the production of saliva is quite low on the body's survival agenda, knowing as it does we are not about to eat a hearty meal as we fight or run from our assailant.

➢ We have an urge to go to the toilet in order to lighten our body weight, again to help us run faster. We can also experience griping stomach cramps, as the need to lighten our body weight spreads to our whole digestive system, sometimes even producing not only nausea but sickness and diarrhoea.

➢ Having made our decision to either fight our neighbour's blaze or run away, our thinking mind will not be needed in the ensuing action so our thinking processes then slow down or become stuck like a record on the same recurring negative thought.

All these symptoms are perfectly normal and in fact can be life-savers in a real emergency. However when the problem is not an actual emergency, simply our thoughts having got a little out of hand, we are suddenly left with all this adrenaline coursing through our veins with nowhere to go. If we are not releasing this energy through physical activity, it continues to course through our blood stream making us feel extremely ill, both mentally and physically. This is what is known as a panic attack. All the symptoms described overwhelm us and we are left literally gasping for breath, heart pounding and the thought "Help, I can't breathe, I'm going to die" repeating over and over in our brain like a stuck record.

At this stage we are immune to someone telling us to calm down. Our physiology has taken over and our rational mind has gone walk-about!

Forewarned is Forearmed!

It is vitally important to understand that all these symptoms, however distressing they feel in the moment, are actually our body reacting in a healthy and normal way, considering it believes there is a disaster looming. Because we are unable to think rationally whilst having a panic attack, it is vital to learn about the fight and flight response and develop some coping strategies while we are calm. We can influence our own thinking much more easily while suffering an attack if we have already learnt that this is purely a stress reaction, it is *not* a physical illness and we are *not* about to die.

Supposing we look out of our window and think our neighbour's house is on fire, jump up and rush to the window, only to discover the smoke is actually coming from a bonfire in the garden. What happens to all those symptoms that had started up in our body as we rushed to the window? Of course, they slowly dissipate, our breathing slows back to a normal rate, our heart stops pounding, and our hands stop shaking. In all it takes about three minutes for the over-arousal to subside, once we have ascertained there isn't a problem. And that is the crucial part of overcoming panic attacks!

However what happens in an actual attack is that we keep repeating the original message of alarm, so we keep re-infecting ourselves with false information. Instead of our body being left to calm down naturally, because of our faulty thinking we continue to repeat to ourselves that there really is a disaster looming, because that is what it feels like.

Challenge the Frightening Thoughts

The first thing we need to do when we recognise the overwhelming feelings of terror encroaching on our awareness, is to press our feet down into the ground, touch the solid seat we are sitting on and look intently around us. This re-establishes ourselves into the safety of the here and now, and helps to dispel the frightening sensations rushing round our bodies. The important part of helping ourselves to overcome panic attacks is to be willing to take on board that we must disregard what we are actually feeling and remember the facts we have learnt about what is really happening i.e. that this is a healthy reaction to the false belief that there is an emergency looming. So we need to repeatedly tell ourselves we are safe, regardless of what it feels like.

Medication

There is a lot of anxiolytic (anxiety reducing) medication available from our G.P., but sometimes a herbal remedy bought over the counter from the pharmacy or even the supermarket can work just as well. It is better to only take this medication when actually going in to a panic attack, rather than taking it three times a day, as it is more effective taken only when needed. If our anxiety becomes so bad that we do need to see the G.P. try asking for a beta-blocker as this will slow the heart rate down thus easing all the other symptoms. It is preferable to a sedative which affects our level of functioning leaving us feeling drowsy. Unfortunately beta-blockers cannot be tolerated by everybody, for example people with diabetes.

When Two and Two Make Five!

Suppose we are going through a very stressful time with our job and at the same time are starting a new relationship. We are out with our new date, and suddenly all the stress of our work situation overwhelms us. We start to feel hot and uncomfortable. We feel very ill and need to go home. We decide we are far too stressed to continue dating, or perhaps our date becomes a great help, and we form a relationship. Eventually we resolve the problem at work and get on with our life. Years later, we are once again on our own and start to date again. However, we find to our horror that we are terrified every time we go out on a date and we can't understand why.

What is happening is that in our unconscious mind we have put two and two together and made five. We are remembering the panic symptoms we had all those years ago, and are associating it with starting a new relationship. However the true cause of our panic back then was the considerable stress we were under at work and the fact we were dating at the time was purely co-incidental. Unfortunately our memory can often play tricks with us. We can suppress painful memories and indeed have highly selective memories. So the more stressful something was, the more likelihood we will have suppressed it.

If we are aware we are connecting feelings of anxiety to a particular incident in our past and are getting anxious every time we find ourselves in a similar situation, we need to check that there was not something else even more stressful going on at that time. We may need to talk to a therapist to help regress us back to this time, to enable us to really begin to understand and heal those painful memories. As long as something is relegated to our unconscious mind, it cannot be healed. Painful as it is to recall awful things that happened to us in the past, it is less painful than keeping them hidden where they wreak havoc, both mentally and physically.

Strategies for Coping with Panic Attacks

1. Repeat over to ourselves like a mantra "I am actually alright. This is only a stress reaction. I am safe." We need to keep this mantra as simple and basic as possible, as we will not remember anything complicated when in the middle of an attack.

2. Remember it will soon pass if we stop frightening ourselves with more scary thoughts.

3. Concentrate on slowing and deepening our breathing, maybe even counting "in 1, 2, 3, 4, out 1, 2, 3, 4, 5, 6, 7" as we focus exclusively on our breathing for several minutes. By making our out-breath slower than our in-breath we are reinforcing the fact that we are safe and can relax. This sends a clear message to our body and mind that all is well, while rapid, shallow breathing sends a message that we need more oxygen because we are facing a problem.

4. Reassure ourselves that in the present moment we are safe. Thinking about what might happen is unhelpful. Look around and ascertain "In this moment I am OK"

5. Accept the scary feelings, watch them come and allow them to go. Don't either hold on to them or fight them. Breathe into them, and breathe them out with each out breath.

6. Consciously drop our shoulders and start to relax our stomach muscles. As we repeat the mantra from step 1, start to relax all of our muscles, beginning at the top of our head and concentrating on each part of the body in turn until we reach our feet. This concentration will stop our mind repeating messages of doom and disaster, which is what it will do if left to its own devices.

7. Write out the simple table below clearly in large letters, keeping it in our purse, wallet or on our bedside table.

---

1. Slowly repeat I AM SAFE over and over

2. Remember it will pass

3. Breath slowly and deeply

4. Look around and stay in the safety of the present moment

5. Accept the scary feelings, breathe into them, let them go

6. Relax all my muscles

7. Repeat steps 1 to 6 until the panic subsides

Using Reverse Therapy

One successful method that can help enormously with panic attacks is Reverse Therapy, which was described in Chapter Four, Body Mind Awareness. This works best if the technique of concentrating on all the sensations in the feet over a ten minute period is practised regularly when calm. Only then does it become such a second-nature response it can easily be brought to mind and utilised when actually feeling panicky.

It seems the reason this is such a successful technique is because when we panic, we tend to "leave our body". Obviously we don't literally do this or we would lose consciousness. However, when having a panic attack, our mind is rushing around in a state of turmoil and our awareness of the actual sensations in our physical body are minimised. This is probably because they are so overwhelming and awful, our body is not a comfortable place to be in! However by slowly and deliberately concentrating on every small sensation in our toes and feet, it literally grounds us, stopping the crazy escalation of scary thoughts in their tracks, and bringing us down to earth and back to reality even quicker than merely telling our selves we are safe.

Post-Traumatic Stress Disorder

If we are already well-aware of the cause of our anxiety and recognise that we have suffered a trauma in the past, we may need to take further action. Years ago one could only be diagnosed with PTSD if one had been in a war zone or a recognized disaster, like a train crash. However it has become increasingly apparent that anyone can suffer in this way if they have experienced something which to them was the equivalent of having the carpet pulled from under them. It is not so much the nature of the incident than the subjective experience of the sufferer that determines whether one is traumatised or not.

EMDR

One of the most recent therapies available, and recognised by the National Institute of Health and Clinical Excellence as the therapy of choice for trauma, is called EMDR or Eye Movement Desensitisation and Reprocessing. The scientific thinking behind the discovery of this very beneficial therapy is that when we suffer trauma a split develops between the functioning in the left and right hemispheres of the brain.

The left brain is the logical, linear-type thinking brain that simply puts the problem behind us and gets on with life. The right brain, or more instinctive, intuitive brain however locks the trauma in an inaccessible place, where even years later it is just as traumatised as it was the instant the trauma was happening. This accounts for flashbacks, nightmares and otherwise unaccountable panic attacks.

By using rapid eye movement in the controlled and supportive environment of the therapist's clinic, the two parts of the brain are able to come together, thus integrating and healing the traumatic memory, drastically reducing its debilitating effect on our life.

Becoming Our Own Expert

As we begin to learn more about the nature of anxiety and, more importantly, the way our particular form of it affects us, we can begin to become our own expert. As discussed at the end of the previous chapter, the NHS is starting up Expert Patient Programs in many areas, so once we have become very familiar and even at home with the often bizarre symptoms we can experience as a direct result of tension, stress, worry and anxiety, we can empower ourselves by becoming our own expert on our particular illness.

This in itself can often lead to the lessening of our symptoms, because it is the very sense of feeling powerless that triggers feelings of anxiety and panic in the first place. Rather than relying totally on the Doctor to cure us with a magic pill, we can begin to work out what we are doing that makes things worse and therefore start to change some of our more negative thoughts, feelings and behaviours. This does not happen overnight, as it has taken us a lifetime to build up the patterns of thought and behaviour that has led to our illness. However, once we decide we are the ones that can ultimately make us well, we can set out, armed with as much information and advice as we can find, on our journey to self-healing and wholeness.

See Reference No 9
EMDR
www.emdr-therapy.org

Part Four

Awareness of Our True Nature

Chapter Twelve

Awareness of the Role of Forgiveness

To many people forgiveness implies backing down, loosing face, failing, admitting defeat or, worse still, something religion and the church tells us to do. The implication is this is something we SHOULD do, not something we WANT to do. However, when looked at through the eyes of therapy, recovery, self-awareness and healing, the role of forgiveness takes on a completely different dimension. When we start to look closely at what the lack of forgiveness does to us, we begin to become aware that this lack only damages ourselves, so we are injured twice, first by the aggressor and secondly by ourselves.

Every time we remember the slight or abuse we suffered at the hand of the aggressor, we are once again filled with the same emotions of hurt, hatred, anger, fear or dread that we had at the time of the incident. Isn't it bad enough they put us through that at the time? Surely we wouldn't CHOOSE to put ourselves through the same ordeal and gamut of emotions repeatedly, over years and years, every time something reminds us of the abuse, would we?

Once we can understand that our lack of forgiveness is only deepening our pain, we begin to see the possibility that we could choose to forgive as an act of self-love and self-healing. In fact our choice to forgive comes from purely selfish reasons: we want to start to feel better. So our choice to forgive is fundamentally for ourselves and has little or nothing to do with the aggressor. It's our life, and we want to get back in the driving seat. So what better way to do it than taking our power back? Previously the aggressor had the power and wielded it against us. Now we have the choice to take back our own power and wield it in such a way that we ensure our own safety, healing and health.

Forgiveness Exercise

Part One –Validation

The first step we need to take is to validate our feelings and discharge every last drop of bitterness, hurt and anger. So for the last time we allow ourselves the time and space to express in writing in our Journal exactly how we felt back then. This is a pre-cursor to being able to move on. If we have never expressed the full extent of our hurt even to ourselves, it is hard to truly let go. We need to express all those negative feelings in one last cathartic release, before we decide to drop them forever. One word of warning. We cannot commence this exercise unless we will have time to complete the entire exercise in one sitting. If we complete the first part only we will be left feeling worse than when we started.

Here are some suggestions for headings to encourage us to truly release our pain, hurt and anger.

- o   This person has taken something from me

- o   I need to defend myself by attacking

- o   I'm not getting what I want

- o   I feel alone and afraid

- o   I am stuck in the pain of the past.

At the end of Part One, it is very clear to us that this is an uncomfortable place to be in and we are ready to choose to move into a more comfortable place inside ourselves.

Part Two

Empathy

Let's take a few minutes to deeply relax, and as we let go, we imagine ourselves becoming lighter. We imagine ourselves floating upwards, and then see ourselves looking down on two people sitting on a beach with an enormous beach ball between them. We can clearly see from our bird's eye view that the ball is red on one side and blue on the other. However we can hear these two people arguing about the colour of the ball. We wonder how we are ever going to get them to understand the truth, that it is both red AND blue. Then we realise that if one of them just got up, leaving their stuck position and just walked around the ball, they too would see the truth. Also we realise that, by being willing to let go of his position, this one has left his place free for the other one to move into, thus freeing up the stalemate.

With this higher perspective in mind we can objectively recall the incident which needs forgiveness. We can take several slow deep breaths and begin to recall the incident in a relaxed and detached manner, as if we were above it looking down on it, as in the above visualisation. We don't label the aggressor, nor feel self-pity. We see the two people in question as separate from ourselves.

Now we start to visualise the event from the perpetrator's point of view. Remember that when people feel stressed they are rarely rational. This is not to invalidate our own feelings and experience. We have already relived this many times from our point of view, but in order to heal we now need to see it from the other's viewpoint too. This will give us a more rounded and whole picture. Now we return to the more impersonal visualisation of the two people and the beach ball. Remaining with this higher perspective we come out of the relaxation and write what we have just experienced in our Journal.

Part Three

Rising Above it!

We now tell ourselves that we can rise above hurt and vengeance. We see ourselves as having reached a stage in our development where we are able to look at life from a new perspective. We are now a big enough person to be able to give ourselves the gift of altruism. So for the third time we return to our Journal and start to write out some new ideas, coming from this new and wider perspective. Each of these comments is the new way of looking at the five comments written about in Part One.

- I now see that every experience has taught me something, and I have grown from it.

- This person was obviously having a really bad time when he/she did that

- My purpose on this planet is to give and receive love

- As I change and grow I feel much more at peace and at one with others

- I now let go of the past and move into living in the present with joy

Part Four

Forgiveness

Now is the time to commit in writing our decision to forgive. We can write out a Declaration of Forgiveness and decide to show this written commitment to one other person, someone we feel close to and can trust. An example is shown at the end of the chapter. You might want to photocopy it and use it or create your own declaration. Fill your name in and the name of the person you are forgiving and then fill in the other blanks as appropriate. Treat it as a legal document.

When memories of the event resurface, let's remind ourselves that we **have** forgiven them, and we are now able to see the past from a new and wider perspective.

There is only one person seriously affected by a lack of forgiveness and that is our self. Let's be prepared to go through this exercise for ourselves, and for our own healing. The perpetrator has hurt us once. Why let them continue to hurt us every time we remember what happened? We are free to forgive and release them, thus releasing ourselves at the same time.

Declaration of Forgiveness

I _____

forgive you _____

I understand that you must have been feeling

_____

and thinking

_____

when you did that to me. From your angle I now see that it looked like

_____

which is why you acted that way. I now commit to forgiving you.

Signed _____

Date _____

Chapter Thirteen

Conclusion - Ending the Case of Mistaken Identity

So what do we mean by "ending the case of mistaken identity"?

Who is the one who is mistaken? And what identity are we talking about?

We are the ones who are mistaken. From early childhood we have believed we are who we are told we are. If we were told repeatedly we are clever / pretty / nice, we think of ourselves as clever / pretty / nice. If we were told repeatedly we were stupid / ugly / horrible, we believe we are stupid / ugly / horrible. Even though situations in life occur that point to the opposite of our internalised identity, we tend to dismiss them as false. Each time a situation occurs that reinforces our belief, it deepens our conviction that of course that is who we are.

And the identity that is mistaken is the one that has contributed to our current depression and anxiety. That is the mistaken identity that somehow deep down inside

ourselves we are deeply flawed. The truth is THAT IS A LIE!
When we look back at the lessons learnt in each of the
preceding chapters, we can see how each of the previous
topics have led us to an increased awareness of our true
nature which no longer needs to identify with our depressed
or anxious feelings.

The first chapter discussed the various self-definitions
that society has given us, then asked us to look deeper into
the fact we may be more than we think we are. We were
introduced to the Aware Observer Self through a
Psychosynthesis exercise, which showed us we are definitely
MORE than we think we are.

Then in the chapter about the Three Faces of Self we
looked at the face we show to the world, the face we hide
from the world, and the face of who we truly are, with an
exercise to discover our three faces, and to once again prove
our deep inner self is in fact good and true.

In the third chapter we used NLP (Neuro Linguistic
Programming) to help us become aware of some of our
limiting beliefs, how they influence our behaviour and
therefore our experience, and how we can start to change
these limiting beliefs.

Next we used Body Mind Awareness to look at the
latest scientific discoveries that point to the connection

between our body and mind. We looked at Reverse Therapy, and how it works by introducing us to the concept of our body's own awareness, helping to overcome chronic fatigue and anxiety.

In the fifth chapter we looked at both Solution Focused Therapy and Positive Psychology, and how these new therapies agree with ancient wisdom about the holistic nature of human beings and the subsequent need for a holistic therapeutic approach.

Next we looked at Cognitive Behavioural Therapy, the therapy recommended by the NICE (National Institute of Health and Clinical Excellence) and available on the NHS, and how it teaches us that our experience happens as a direct result of how we think and feel. We saw how important it is to challenge negative thoughts, as invariably those thoughts are frightening us with worst-case scenarios, rather than telling us the truth about ourselves or the situation we find ourselves in. We also learnt how to build new coping strategies, helping us to take charge of our life.

In chapter seven we discovered Mindfulness Awareness. This is an ancient Buddhist practise now taken up by psychotherapists and used by the NHS to run courses for people suffering severe stress due to physical or mental illness. We learnt that by becoming mindful of our negative thoughts, feelings and behaviour patterns, we become more able to let them go, choosing to feel and think in a healthier manner.

Then we discovered that through understanding basic assertiveness principles such as The Bill of Rights we could embrace some new life skills with which to combat depression and stress.

We went on to understand anger and how depression and anxiety can be exacerbated by suppressing our anger. We also looked at understanding the therapeutic nature of anger when used appropriately. We learnt how to manage our anger and looked at how we actually experience our own anger and then how we can learn to de-escalate our anger by managing it successfully.

Next we learnt how to understanding depression, looking at the nature of depression, how our thoughts perpetuate it, and how to change our biochemistry, not just with anti-depressant medication but also by changing the way we look at life in general through increasing our awareness of who we are.

We then learnt how to understanding anxiety by looking at the physical symptoms associated with anxiety, how they arise, and how to work with them. We also learnt about the Fight/Flight Response, and how to use CBT,

Reverse Therapy or EMDR to change our approach to anxiety.

And lastly we began to understand the role of forgiveness by looking at how a lack of forgiveness only damages ourselves, so we are injured twice, first by the aggressor and secondly by ourselves. We saw how we choose to forgive as an act of self-love and self-healing.

So can we now see why this chapter is called "Ending the Case of Mistaken Identity"? WE NEVER WERE THE BAD OR USELESS PERSON WE USED TO THINK WE WERE….. IT WAS A LIE, STARTED BY UNAWARE PEOPLE IN OUR CHILDHOOD AND DEEPENED BY OWN MISUNDERSTANDING ABOUT WHO WE ARE!

Finally we can see how each of the previous topics has led us to an increased awareness of our true nature. We no longer need to identify with our depressed or anxious feelings thus changing these feelings and ourselves for ever.

So if you are not who you thought you were, WHO ARE YOU? Enjoy discovering!

About the author

Emma trained as an occupational therapist in London forty years ago. Having qualified she decided to specialize in mental health and her working life started at York Clinic, Guys Hospital. Here she began running encounter groups and started to understand the importance of talking through worrying issues.

From here Emma began to study newer approaches to health, including Psychosynthesis. This was the first time she became aware of the holistic approach, realizing the importance of including spiritual awareness alongside psychological growth. Emma had already been practicing yoga and meditation for some years.

She had a few years out to raise her family, during which time her interests widened into studying ancient wisdom, philosophy, healing and personal development. She travelled widely, spending time in India, New Zealand and America.

Emma set up and ran a Stress Management business, and later studied Life Coaching. On returning to work in a psychiatric clinic, she was delighted to find many of her colleagues had developed along similar lines, and her once rather avant-garde views were now becoming more mainstream. Whilst working in the NHS she continued her training by qualifying as an NLP practitioner, and studying Solution Focused Brief Therapy and also Mindfulness. She has been delighted to introduce all of the therapies discussed in this book to her clients, with rewarding results.